Arthur H. Carhart

is nationally recognized as a leader among conservationists. Born in Mapleton, Iowa, in 1892, he received a B.S. in landscape architecture and city planning from Iowa State College in 1916. After serving with the medical corps in World War I, he joined the U.S. Forest Service as its first permanent landscape architect in 1919. Four years later he resigned to engage in private pr.ctice as a professional landscape architect and city planner, and began his long and productive career as a writer of books and magazine articles on conservation and the outdoor life. In 1938 he was appointed director of the program for Federal Aid in Wildlife Restoration in Colorado. Arthur Carhart's many books include *The Outdoorsman's Cookbook* (1944) and *Fresh Water Fishing* (1950). He won the Founder's Award of the Izaak Walton League for his *Water—or Your Life* (1951) and *Timber in Your Life* (1955), and the first annual award of the Outdoor Writers of America Association for his various writings about conservation.

THE NATIONAL FORESTS

THE
NATIONAL
FORESTS

BY

ARTHUR H. CARHART

WITH AN INTRODUCTION BY

JOSEPH W. PENFOLD

CONSERVATION DIRECTOR
IZAAK WALTON LEAGUE OF AMERICA

NEW YORK   ALFRED A. KNOPF

1959

L. C. CATALOG CARD NUMBER: 59–5433

© ARTHUR H. CARHART, 1959

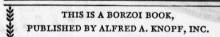

THIS IS A BORZOI BOOK,
PUBLISHED BY ALFRED A. KNOPF, INC.

FIRST EDITION

INTRODUCTION

I LIKE the way Arthur Carhart writes about natural resources. Beyond that, I like the national forests, and that's what his book is about. In it you will find data and statistics because forests are made up of board feet, acre feet, animal unit months, annual increments, carrying capacities of livestock, wildlife, even people. The forests are sagebrush flats, pinyon-juniper, aspen, pine, spruce-fir, or something else. They are Upper Sonoran, Canadian, Arctic, or some other label that scientists give them—not to confuse, but striving for a preciseness that they know must be attained to achieve full understanding of ecological forces.

The national forests are watersheds, and Arthur Carhart gives this aspect particular emphasis, because it is the least dramatic, most of the time—and the most important in the long run everywhere.

You will find much more in the book because the author knows the forests. He has lived with them and by them. Like a thousand others over the past half-century who have been active in the Forest Service, he is jealous of his part because a forest is a personal experience. So it is for all others who have a bit of sensitivity in their souls and who have "lived" even briefly in the forested outdoors.

Such thoughts crowded my mind as I read the manuscript while driving from Denver to the eastern seaboard. More exactly, my wife read it aloud. I drove. This procedure is guaranteed to shorten the most tedious trip. Not that I find unexciting the drive down the South Platte Valley to Ogallala, where the North and South Plattes join, then eastward along the Platte to Omaha and the Missouri. Through irrigated pastures, fields of sugar beets and corn. Past cattle feed lots, alfalfa-dehydration plants, taut little cities and towns, trim school buildings, grain elevators, lumber yards, and outdoor salesrooms bright with new farm machinery.

It is a green belt of production, giving strength to the economy and culture of a wide region. Its roots lie in the forested mountains to the west, and its influence stretches clear to the Mississippi and beyond. It is the river which gives present meaning and a future to this valley, and the national forests have been dedicated to assure that there will always be the river. And so it is in a hundred other valleys.

The South Platte has its birth in the national-forest snow fields which ring Colorado's scenic 9,500-foot valley, South Park—the Bayou Salado of the early trappers. From these high basins and forested slopes comes moisture to support the grass and livestock of the valley, to feed industry and sprinkle the lawns of Denver. Below Denver other streams, Clear Creek, Boulder, St. Vrain, Big Thompson, Cache la Poudre, gathered along the peaks and forests of the Front Range, join it to bring their miracle of water far out into the low-rainfall prairies.

The North Platte rises in North Park, Colorado—again a high valley, ringed, except for its escape canyon, by the peaks and ridges of the Routt, Arapahoe, Roosevelt, and Medicine Bow national forests. Joined later by the Laramie, which originates on the incomparable Rawah Wild Area, the North Platte courses through Casper, Wyoming, where it nourishes the business and industry of that fast-growing city. Above and below Casper, important storage at Seminoe, Pathfinder, Alcova, Glendo, Guernsey, and McConnaghy dams delays its flow but adds increasingly to its usefulness.

The timber, cattle, and other products of national-forest lands exert their influence clear along the Platte Valley and along all the other important valleys of the West, but the streams themselves provide that constant link between all of civilization's component parts.

So my wife read; I drove and listened, and as we caught a glimpse of the river through the cottonwoods, or crossed it, I could nod my head in recognition and say: "I knew you when. . . .

"You were a willow-screened beaver pond in South Park where my son caught his first trout." I'd packed him on my back out to an old beaver house, rigged up his rod, and left him to his own devices as I went about mine. When next I checked, he had that wriggling minnow clasped to his chest and a beatific look on his face that meant another dedicated outdoorsman had been christened.

Another day high in the Rawah, he, his brother, and I hiked up and down valleys, over saddles, around shoulders of the mountains to enjoy a dozen forest-circled, jewel-like lakes, casting a fly more to see if the trout would rise than to take the fish. Back at camp we could catch a panful while the cook-type member of the group got the fire burning well.

Or on the east slope of the Routt. We had left the pack train, ridden over timberline grazing lands, through the spruce, down among rock piles and lush meadows to Roxy Ann Lake to spend a coffee or two with friends camped there. A lovely place, remote, almost untouched by man.

"You were Rock River on the 'Bow where some thoughtless fisherman left his campfire unextinguished and caused a holocaust. You weren't so pretty that day as the plane carried us over your ash-covered slopes and the still smoking snags that had been your forest a few days before."

On down the Platte and across the Missouri—then a thousand river miles from its sources on the Beaverhead, Gallatin, and Deer Lodge. A thousand miles from the Lewis and Clark and its Bob Marshall Wilderness—an incomparable country. A place of elk, whitetail, muledeer, moose, grizzly, black bear, bighorn sheep, mountain goats, and a host of smaller mammals.

A long, long way from Lake Solitude in the Big Horn.

"I knew you when," I might say to the Big Muddy. "You were a marshy pond under the Chinese Wall where a big bull moose lifted his dripping head to watch us pass. You were nothing but a tiny spring dropping into Solitude where we cooled our butter in your frigid waters and slaked our thirst. You were Jakey's Fork on the Shoshone, Reno Gulch in the Black Hills, and a hundred other national-forest streams, large and small, finding their way to the Missouri and Mississippi."

The Missouri River at Omaha is a long way from national-forest watersheds, but on them, nonetheless, originates a full half of its flow. They are in fact, as well as in name, "national" forests. So, likewise, are the Sequoia in California, the Ouachita in Arkansas, the Superior in Minnesota, the Allegheny in Pennsylvania, and the Jefferson in Virginia. One hundred and forty-nine national forests in all, comprising 180 million acres.

The author has written of the forests and their multiple resources and uses in terms of people—those who had the vision to establish them, the generations of foresters who have given dedicated service to their management, and the increasing millions of us who use them directly for a variety of purposes or whose lives are beneficially affected by them. This is good, because the national forests are indeed an essential ingredient of the American culture. You will understand your national forests better and appreciate them more as you travel with Arthur Carhart through these pages.

Joseph W. Penfold
Conservation Director,
Izaak Walton League of America

FOREWORD

THE magnitude of the national forests is reflected in the great array of official files and publications pertaining to them. How many forest folk helped in gathering memoranda, pamphlets, data, and incidents from which material for this book was selected, I cannot estimate. In collecting basic material, the scores of whom I have knowledge were helped by many whose names I do not know—a forest clerk, a ranger, an assistant to a divisional chief in a regional office. The true spirit of the U.S.F.S. is demonstrated in teamwork and dedication to the job to be done. I had help from these people of the forest, from many, many points, and to all these I must express my sincere gratitude for aid they gave gladly and freely.

Arthur H. Carhart

CONTENTS

CONTENTS

ILLUSTRATIONS

ALL PHOTOGRAPHS COURTESY OF
U.S. FOREST SERVICE

FOLLOWING PAGE 80

FOLLOWING PAGE 176

[xiii]

THE NATIONAL FORESTS

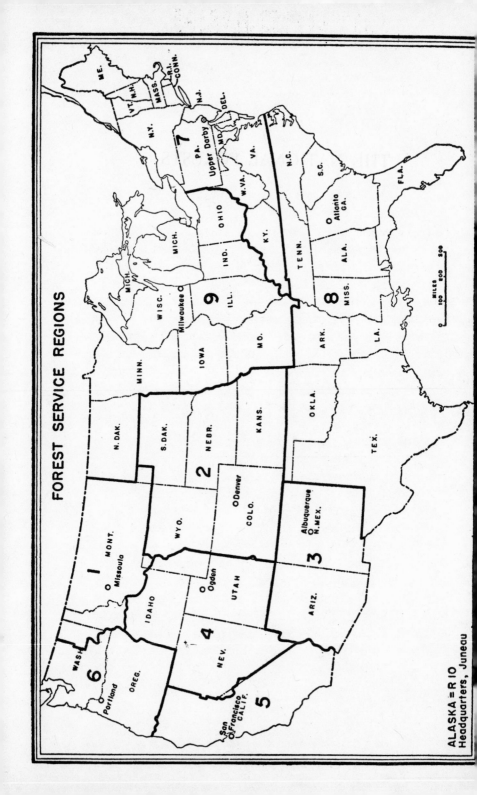

FOREST SERVICE REGIONS

ALASKA = R 10
Headquarters, Juneau

I

OUR FOREST HERITAGE

I

NEITHER science nor magic can compress the more than 180,000,000 acres of our national forests within the covers of a book. The forests are vast. The Tongass in Alaska alone contains 16,016,666 acres—larger than ten Delawares. The Tonto National Forest in Arizona, largest in the continental United States, contains 2,902,473 acres—or about two and one third times the acreage of New Jersey. The area of all national forests exceeds that of Texas by about 10,000,000 acres.

Most of our national forests are in western states. During the period when the majority of them were first dedicated to public use, the unreserved and unappropriated territory available for such dedication was in rough, non-agricultural highlands west of the Great Plains.

Later in the chronicles of national-forest history, Congress passed measures that permitted the purchase of various lands in eastern states with which national forests were assembled. Recently the forests first established registered a half century of existence. At the time of the anniversary the U.S. Forest Service had responsibilities in administering lands in 44 states, Hawaii, and Puerto Rico.

Within the national forests is a great diversity in land forms, soil types, tree associations, and wild-flower communities. Each has its complement of animate woodland residents. And though there is diversity throughout the

[3]

whole, you will find that at any time in a specific place each parcel of forest will have its individual unity.

This unity may include one forest or several, a large or a small watershed, or it may be limited to the glade-like valley of a brook. Whichever of these it may be, the unit will have its own unique personality.

A way to gauge the unity of any portion of the forest is to judge whether or not it would be complete should any of its main attributes be lacking. For the forest in its various phases and moods is not a collection of physical things that by chance happen to be lodged in one location. Each part of the community is rightly a member of the whole. If it were not, nature's laws would eventually but surely oust it from the scene.

We should emphasize that this is a book about national *forests*, not national *parks*. There is considerable confusion in the minds of many as to which is which and why there is a difference. The national parks were established to protect the finest examples of America's scenic splendors, to preserve special features of scientific and historical worth, and to provide recreational areas for the people of the United States. Exploitation of resources that exist in the national *parks*—development of water power, mining, or harvesting of timber, for example—is prohibited.

The national *forests*, though they contain all those natural attributes given total protection within the national-park system, are set aside basically to accomplish two quite different objectives: the production of timber that is to be harvested and processed to serve the public, and the protection of vital watersheds. In general, utilization of any other natural resources and other uses that do not interfere with timber production and maintenance of watershed values are allowed in the forests. Recreational use, which is permissible under this policy, has become almost as great in the forests as in the parks, if the number of people visiting them is the measure.

The first part of the name applied to these big properties, the word "national," should not confuse anyone. It should be clear that these are publicly owned forests; every United States citizen holds an interest in these properties. Title to this realty is held in trust for us by the federal government. A federal agency, the U.S. Forest Service, is responsible for the protection and management of these forests.

The word "forest" may demand more examination and discussion. It is a word that generates different concepts in each mind.

Neither you nor I have the same mental picture, when we think of "forest." And neither does the silviculturist, tie-hack, hydrologist, skier, charcoal-burner, or ornithologist. These varying thought pictures are based on personal experiences, particular individual interests, and knowledge acquired from reading, lectures, or perhaps viewing motion pictures with woodland backgrounds.

Most people revise their ideas of what these forests are like only after they have seen them. I had always carried an image of a solid stand of mature, first-growth trees, stretching without a break to the horizon. But in my first encounters with national forests, I had to revise my concept.

Early in 1919 I returned from Army duty in World War I to join the U.S. Forest Service as its first fulltime landscape designer. During four years my job was to develop policies and plans for recreational uses on 23,-000,000 acres of wildlands scattered in six states. My headquarters were in Denver. My first field trip to acquaint me with the forests of the region began with a chilly, fog-blinded ride in an oldtime open touring-car up the canyon of Clear Creek west of Denver. I was accompanied by three old hands, forest officers in what was then called Districts. The mists were opaque curtains between us and the canyon's depths. Darkness had further obscured the surroundings as we halted at the Empire ranger station to spend the night.

Next morning the cloudless sunrise revealed fire-scarred ridges and slopes where early miners had burned off timber in order to locate ore veins more readily. A few old ponderosa pines and Douglas firs had survived the flames. If one searched, seedling trees could be found sheltering in the brushy cover that had sprung up following the fires. The cradles of new forests were tucked into the little side canyons and draws; the infant trees were swaddled in twiggy bushes and the lower-growing grasses.

Many people believe that a century may pass before a completely new forest can reclaim a fire-swept area. But within three decades many mountain sides along Clear Creek—which were all but treeless in 1919—would gradually become cloaked with fine young firs and pines. But that first view of Clear Creek canyon in the Pike National Forest (now in the Arapaho) radically modified my earlier notions about the type of woodlands with which I would be working in my land-use planning.

Succeeding trips took me to other national forests. Much of what I saw was contrary to my earlier ideas of what a forest should be. Still, I could not wholly discard a belief that there were old and stately forests such as the one Robin Hood and his men called home. It was mid-June of that first year before I found a tree-blanketed valley that did resemble a storybook forest.

Bill Thomas, a forest guard, had guided me along saddle trails to the upper basin of Bear Creek, which fans out across the eastern slopes of the mountain mass topped by

Mount Evans, the 14,260-foot peak dominating the skyline
west of Denver. Bill unloaded my duffel at a log cabin not
far below timberline, and for a week I tramped marked
trails, game traces, and trackless stretches within the Bear
Creek basin. Fat white clouds roved the blue sky on the
June day as I swung along the Lost Creek trail and suddenly found a living forest that fitted perfectly my original
image of a woodland as a solid stand of timber.

Venerable Engelmann spruces stood high beside the
pathway. The shadowy corridors between trees were silent.
I had not yet learned that deep forest has fewer bird and
animal residents than the margins between timber and
meadow. But as I returned to the cabin I saw that an in-
quisitive wildcat, which I never glimpsed, had left paw
marks in the footprints I had made in the soft earth.

In other places I found similar forests. Ponderosa pines
with orange boles reared high on slopes of South Dakota's
Black Hills. Other old pines festooned the tablelands of
New Mexico and Arizona. Thickets of mighty Douglas firs,
each straight-boled tree rising more than a hundred feet,
clustered on the mountains of Oregon and Washington.
Along the clear lakes through which runs the imaginary line
between Ontario and Minnesota majestic old white pines
were mirrored in the still waters. Quaking aspens found a
happy residence on the western slopes of Wyoming's Snowy
Range, their straight, thick trunks rising sheer without limbs
for sixty or more feet.

But for the greater part of my four years of journeying in
Region 2 of the U.S.F.S., I hiked across the dry, gravelly
slopes flanking Colorado's Poudre Canyon, the treeless
arctic tundra above timberlines in Wyoming, and across
Minnesota, where I saw the brush and scrub timber that
rose above ashes left when rampant logging followed the
pattern of cut, slash, and burn, which characterized opera-

tions of most lumber companies during the nineteenth century.

The one certainty about the national forests is that they do not consistently conform to any fixed standards. There are many more acres of burned-over land with second growth on them, more tundra, sparsely wooded acres, grassy slopes, and great stretches of brush than there are big-tree timberlands. These areas are no less interesting than solidly timbered forests; these areas often are as vital to us as if they were covered with continuous ranks of saw-log timber. Though there will always be many acres of non-commercial timber in the national forests, each year shows a change-over in large areas from scrub to potential sawlog timber.

There are relatively few areas of forests we may call "virgin." Because they represent fully mature stands typical of yesterday's timberlands, there is justification for protecting and maintaining a selected number of these units in undamaged condition. It is true that the national parks contain and preserve typical old timber stands. But the parks do not encompass every type of forest community found across the continent. Additional natural living museums of unscarred woods within the national forests are needed to supplement those of the parks.

Blocks of ancient forests can show, by contrasts with logged-over lands, the patterns of life found where only nature's laws have ruled. Often, leaving nature undisturbed in some representative areas will lead to better practices in managing millions of woodland acres of public forests as well as properties in commercial "tree farms." We are not so desperately in need of lumber now—nor should we be within the near future—that we cannot afford a reasonable number of such sanctuaries, where life associations are much like what they were throughout this continent before we voracious humans began consuming the wood-lands' bounty. But we must accept most of our national-forest areas for what they are—lands dedicated primarily to serving material needs in our daily living.

I I

WE HAVE about 150 national forests. This is an approxi-mate number. For several reasons, including pressure from Congress to economize, the Forest Service has developed a proclivity for welding two forests together under one ad-ministrative staff and one name, or for carving up one forest and pasting its parts into several other forests. When this happens a name and an administrative unit disappear from organization charts. No acreage is changed. It is a paper demise only.

I have lost several old friends through these administra-tive executions. The Washakie National Forest of Wyo-ming, always a favorite of mine—partly because it was a name-monument to a great Indian—now is merged with the Shoshone Forest. I still think of the Washakie as it was, with its own history. But Washakie was a Shoshone statesman, and his shade may be pleased that his tribe's name was retained for the augmented forest. And so it has been with the Cochetopa, Leadville, Holy Cross, Monte-zuma, and other forests that were separate units when I first followed trails through them and are now parts of en-larged forests bearing other names.

A review of the more important resources of the national forests and of the use to which this natural wealth is put will expand understanding of what the forests are and for what reasons they exist.

A lumberman glances first no doubt at hillsides clothed with thick ranks of mature fir, pine, or spruce. He sees the full-grown trees as a crop, ripe for harvest. He mentally calculates the potential board feet of lumber in each timber stand. He traces with a speculative eye where access roads might be built to get out sawlogs. He may think of the number of houses which could be built with lumber from the trees. Though many lumbermen might also see and appreciate other beauties and treasures of the forest, their first thoughts are of ripe timber and board feet.

There are some who will lodge immediate protests against assigning even a paper priority to timber production. Protection of watersheds, they will insist, is no less vital. And what of the wildlife on these reserves? How about domestic stock-grazing on the grasslands scattered between stands of timber?

Among those who have an interest in the services that forests afford, none is more insistent that his use be served than the recreationist. The millions who seek the forests to camp, picnic, mountain climb, ski, hunt, and fish will force inclusion of their interests in any management plans.

All these are important forest uses. Which one merits an exact precedence is not so important as that all shall be given fair consideration in plans and policies.

Very early in the forest-conservation movement two most important objectives were defined. Two groups of pioneering conservationists long campaigned for the establishment of a system of federal forests. Almost from Colonial times one band of far-seeing people warned that unless measures were taken to perpetuate the timber supply a day would come when the nation would face a timber shortage. The second group was especially emphatic in demanding a system of public forests to protect the watersheds of our major streams to prevent floods.

The combined pressures of these groups finally maneuvered Congress into passing laws that began the national-
forest system. The Act of March 3, 1891, fixed the authority of the President to "set apart and reserve" the public
forests. The law of June 4, 1897, clearly stated the objectives of these reservations:

"No public forest reservation shall be established, except to
improve and protect the forest within the reservation, or for
the purpose of securing favorable conditions of water flows, and
to furnish a continuous supply of timber for the use and necessities of citizens of the United States; . . ."

The national forests exist, then, to protect watershed
values and to produce wood for the use of the people. We
must accept the fact that our forests were reserved for
these two utilitarian purposes.

At the time the first forests were proclaimed, early in
1891, the census-takers reckoned the country's population
at 63,000,000. With expert management, the acreage now
in the national forests might have supplied that number of
people with sufficient wood for uses then current. Should
every acre in the federal forests now be put under the most
intensive management, they still would not meet today's
needs for wood.

Within recent years about 10 per cent of the United
States' wood requirements, about 6,000,000,000 board feet
per year, has been harvested from the national forests.
Enough timber does come out of the public forests to act
as a stabilizing influence in the timber industry. Some
major timber companies could not operate if they were not
able to purchase national-forest stumpage. Often such supplies are key portions in long-range cutting cycles, which
assure continued operation of companies that do not own

enough land to keep their processing-plants running at capacity.

Of high significance to these companies and to us, the owners of the national forests, is the prospect that much more wood will be harvested from these in years ahead. In fact, trees grown to useful size since the forests were established have only recently become ready for harvest.

Prior to the establishment of many of our federal forests most virgin timber in them had been cut over—logs from the best species taken to the mills—and, because of the bad methods loggers used, woods at large were left in a bad state. Owners forsook the land. In many counties records were clogged with listings of delinquent taxes on timberlands. Uncontrolled wildfire roved the wounded woodlands. Little seedlings were killed, and often the ancient cull trees, left standing because they could not be sawed into good boards, were consumed. These old ones could have served as seed trees had not the recurrent fires destroyed them.

Fire control began when the forest reserves were proclaimed. Almost unnoticed at first, small trees began to fight their way above the weeds and brush that had rushed in to heal the burned-over land. Millions of other acres where natural reseeding was hopeless have been planted with young trees. More and more good stands of trees are rising on lands once fire-scoured and desolated. In some locations the embryo forests are no more than started toward recapturing the land. At other places many acres of second-growth timber soon will be large enough to harvest. It has taken a long time for this to come about, but through the dynamics of growing trees, the national forests are approaching a goal Congress defined more than a half century ago—they should be self-supporting. Sales of timber are now the greatest source of income.

The first congressional reason for establishing the national forests cannot be misunderstood: the production of wood.

The second objective perhaps must increasingly be given the highest primacy in forest management. It is the maintenance of those conditions on many important watersheds which will collect and deliver good water. It has been shown repeatedly that forested slopes provide the most favorable conditions for gathering and delivering usable water.

Within the limitations of laws, appropriations, and the minor fumblings that always beset a large government agency, the U.S. Forest Service has made genuine progress in managing timber in the national forests. The U.S.F.S. has carried on voluminous research in watershed management. There are basins within the national forests in which the growth above the ground surface, and the soil itself, provide excellent conditions for collecting and delivering sustained flows of good water to streams below. Nevertheless, in the entire sweep of water-collecting basins for which it is responsible, the Forest Service has not given watershed management its due consideration.

Most experts agree that the most efficient watershed is the one with reasonably well-maintained forest cover. Trees trap snow and shade drifts, enabling moderate melting to seep into the ground; limbs, twigs, and leaves break the impact of pelting rains so that a downpour hits the forest floor gently and percolates into ground storage. The well-managed watershed has a duff-blanketed floor underneath the tree canopy, with the ground surface so open and grainy that most rainfall and snowmelt is caught and channeled into deep aquifers, the underground strata where percolating waters gather.

It is generally true that if the watershed's slopes are kept in timber stands, its ability to function well is automatically maintained. On the other hand, the grazing of privately owned livestock is often grievously detrimental to watershed values. Nonetheless, the needs of livestock owners have often had more attention and consideration by the Forest Service than has the primary responsibility the Service bears, which is to place watershed maintenance on a par with timber management and above all other forest uses. Grazing on the national forests has received much more attention than it merits for a simple reason: it is a money interest. The direct users of the forage resource have a keen personal interest in that resource, and they have been vocal and demanding. The general public receives the benefits from water conservation. Although adequate and good water is a life essential, the public is remote from the land areas that gather and deliver the water to our communities. Scant water may deplete community bank accounts of more dollars than are received by grazing forest lands, but people do not immediately feel the hurt from watershed losses. Hence few have demanded that more attention be given to water-resource management in our national forests. So long as the faucet flows the public does not concern itself very actively with water problems.

But let the faucet gurgle and drip to dryness, the pump suck air instead of water, crops wilt and the earth become thirsty while brittle tumbleweeds pack into dusty irrigation ditches—then near-panic appears in our conversations and cries out at us from news headlines.

Even when panic rises as water becomes desperately short, the public demonstrates a meager understanding of the watershed's fundamental position in supplying water. It gives little thought to how a river's collecting-basin gathers precipitation, filters, and then delivers water to brooks, rivers, and ultimately to community pipelines. It does not think of wells as dependent on rain and snowmelt captured by porous topsoil and directed into hidden channels that take it to points of pumping. It has not as yet given the watershed the attention it merits in intelligent water-use planning.

Instead a federal engineering agency is called on to draw blueprints and Congress is asked to appropriate a few hundred million dollars for big dams, located where massive floods gather and roar down the main channel and designed to "tame" the deluge by sheer mass of earth fill and solid concrete. No one seems to listen to the voice that says quietly: "If there were myriad leaves, twigs, and forest duff on the slopes of the watershed, these would serve as billions of little dams that would check the freshets before they could run down swiftly to form a flood."

Where sky water falls on bare, skinned slopes, there is little to prevent it from racing to join other frantic water tumbling down gullies and creeks toward the rivers. Then headlines tell of the flood damage, that is, the downstream damage. Rarely is there any mention of the losses of basic wealth, the topsoil robbed of inches of fertility, which occur all over the high basins—there is where the greatest damage is done. Good forest cover, however, will prevent such damage.

Congress gave statutory dignity to only these two forest objectives; the lawmakers considered these as justification for including millions of acres in national reserves. The other uses—recreation, hunting, fishing, the grazing of domestic stock—are merely "permissive."

The grazing of privately owned livestock—cattle, sheep, goats, and horses—on national-forest lands is only one of the permissive uses. But it is a utilitarian use, and it may be grouped for that reason with water and wood procured from the forest. The proper use of the forage crop must be carefully integrated with the timber and water production. Otherwise these two primary values in the forests may suffer grave injury. For these reasons we may properly consider grazing before discussing other permissive uses.

Grazing has another legitimate claim for receiving early attention. It was fairly well established on many parts of the national forests before they were created, and therefore has historical precedence.

For many years most of the trees in national forests have been growing toward sizes large enough to harvest. Until they attained size they could not be sold and revenue utilized. Timber sales only recently became the leading source of revenue, while grazing for many years stood first in national-forest income.

A storm of controversy which swirled around grazing on the forests during the late 1940s and into the 1950s has tended overly to magnify its true importance in management plans. Grazing is a proper use of forest resources. Forage is an annual crop, and harvesting this annual resource can best be accomplished by livestock. The resulting material benefit can be reduced to hard figures.

In contrast, trees may require from forty years to a century or more of growth before they bring the highest return in dollars. Income and the contribution to local economy shows up quicker in cropping grass than in cropping trees. All these factors have tended to secure grazing priority in Forest Service planning and programs.

The great trail drives from Texas had spread herds of cattle across the plains to the foothills and into many mountain valleys before President Cleveland signed the "forest reserve" law of 1891. The sheep had arrived in the west with the Spanish colonists as early as the latter half of the sixteenth century. Sheep and cattle wintered in the lower country, but as grass greened on the hills, the animals were moved to the mountain meadows. The pattern was fixed by the pastoral communities of Spanish colonials in New Mexico, Arizona, and California long before the pioneer cattle ranches appeared on the western scene.

The grazing of the "public domain" on a first-come-first-served basis and without charge—was the accepted custom throughout the western states. When the first rangers rode out to initiate some form of range management on these old lands, they found many pioneer ranchers entrenched on the "free range" that now had been proclaimed "forests." At first there was little control of those rugged livestock operators.

In 1905 the "forest reserves" became national forests, and the old "Bureau of Forestry" became the U.S. Forest Service, largely through efforts of Theodore Roosevelt, Gifford Pinchot, and their associates. Technical foresters took charge of the forests, and they looked on grazing as being basically incompatible with the growing of timber. The 1891 law held no provision for allowing livestock to enter the reserves. Stockmen who continued grazing their animals on these lands were therefore technically in trespass.

That year, 1905, was one of great change in the history of our national forests. Before then the Bureau of Forestry in the Department of Agriculture had been limited to offering technical advice to the General Land Office, a part of the Department of the Interior, for the G.L.O. to that time had had field administration of the forest reserves. There had been no regulation of grazing on the "reserves."

So the animals were on the lands as the new Forest Service took charge. The tradition of the west held that the public domain was "free range." What force could a paper signed by an office-holder on the banks of the Potomac have in barring the sheep of a determined rancher in Idaho or the cows and steers of a Colorado cattleman from hill-sides and valleys where they had grazed unhindered for a decade or more before? The first-comers on the mountain livestock ranges dug in with the intention of staying right there and running the animals on the federal lands regardless of the names that had been tacked on them. That attitude has persisted among many stockmen permitted to use the forests.

The pressure for extensive grazing lands in the forests constantly increased as barbed wire, plow furrows, and more liberal homestead laws squeezed the unfenced acres of the public domain to smaller and smaller size. As new homesteads entered the plains, owners of additional domestic animals desired forest-grazing permits. They often resorted to fervid appeals to congressional delegations if they did not get what they wanted. They succeeded in overloading many ranges, and they still fight frantically against any reduction in numbers of stock permitted.

Thus a dominant obstacle in regulating livestock on the forests can be charged to the character of the stockmen themselves. They fought blizzards, wolves, Indians, and their own kind to establish "rights" on the range. No dude in a new uniform was going to deny them these "rights." Let the rangers try to enforce regulations; men who hung rustlers forthwith could handle a few greenhorn officials trying to enforce regulations.

Technical reasons for limiting the grazing of domestic animals on the forests lay behind some of Pinchot's early directives. Hoofs, said the silviculturists, tended to compact the earth and make it less permeable, and, by reducing insoak of rainfall, lowered the efficiency of watersheds. More important and valid was the foresters' insistence that forage channeled into bellies of sheep and cattle was adding little humus to the land. Watershed values, having high priority in the new laws, could be damaged by excessive grazing.

Officials who tried to secure some control over grazing generally failed. Even after livestock were permitted on designated areas of the forests under the 1897 laws, grazing was legally allowed only in the Pacific Northwest coastal area, west of the crests of the Cascade mountains. High precipitation in that zone assured resurgent plant growth so lush that the organic sponge in topsoil would be adequately maintained.

But those early stockgrowers felt they had "rights" to the forage in the reserves. At times their opposition to regulation often came close to range war. Very early, however, some ranchers recognized regulated grazing as common-sense range management. Then their children went to college and came home with degrees in animal husbandry, range management, or allied subjects. The younger ranchers saw clearly what some of the older heads never would face: maintenance of good watersheds that provide water for irrigated hay meadows in valley bottoms was more important than grazing the high country too heavily. Clearvisioned oldtimers and younger ranchers with technical schooling have worked co-operatively with officials toward balanced use of forage in the national forests. They now are the majority among those who hold forest-grazing permits.

A vociferous minority who contend that the grazing of private livestock on public lands, forests included, is theirs by "right" may always beset the forest officials. They have organization and political prestige, along with loud voices. But forest grazing has a relatively minor position in the livestock industry as a whole. It is a relatively minor factor in the western livestock business. This being so, it must be kept a permissive use subservient to other uses of greater

value to the public. Thus the third utilitarian purpose of
the national forests is rightfully permitted on the forests so
long as greater values are not damaged.

Other material values are secured from the forests. Char-
coal, turpentine, holly and mistletoe for holiday decora-
tions, ferns for florists, wild furs, honey—these suggest the
minor and often interesting permissive uses. All of these
are renewable resources. With sound management, crop
after crop can be had with no harm resulting to water and
timber.

Non-renewable resources also exist within the forests.
Fine or base metals, other minerals, gravel for roads, and
building-stone are materials in this general category. Where
the benefits to the public exceed long-range losses, the re-
moval of such materials is justified.

Sometimes, however, immediate profits and some benefits that result from mining and similar operations are
questionable if measured by the yardstick of time. For
example, a gold dredge operating in a mountain valley will
chew its way through meadows and pastures that are key
acres in a mountain ranch property. Such land grows hay
for winter and supplies early and late season pasturage,
with the adjacent hillsides serving as summer range. Private lands must be purchased by a gold-dredging company
before it works through them, but placer mining laws permit this type of enterprise to operate on national-forest
lands. As the good soil goes through the dredge, the key-
stone of some local ranch often is destroyed.

The gold is washed out from earth and gravel and
caught in the dredge. The fertile soil sluices down the
mountain stream to clog lower channels. Sterile rock
fields, made up of boulders too large to wash away, then
fill the valley floor. The once attractive valley becomes an
industry's dumpgrounds. Once green acres remain desolate,

and for many decades the annual contribution of the valley to human food supplies and other services is entirely lost.

Recreation, the fourth use of the national forests, is the most direct and personal one available to the majority of the citizen-owners.

In years past strange, localized resistance to this use was evident. Visitors to the national forests began to arrive in numbers after the first world war. The roads were made passable to the then new motor cars, which took people into back country formerly available only to the hardy who enjoyed roughing it.

As late as the 1920s, novice tourists drove their chugging gas-wagons to camping spots and there made their own crude rock fireplaces of loose rocks. Mountain country cattle, accustomed to seeing only people astride western saddles, were terrified by human beings on foot. Stockmen complained of "dudes running the fat off the cows," and some stockmen groups actually lodged formal protests against tourists being allowed in the forests. A few old-timers still grumble about tourists scaring the range cattle. This is mostly habit; present-day range livestock is more likely to be a nuisance to campers than to be frightened by them.

Some foresters also grumbled a little because tourists were flooding into back country in the 1920s. Foresters were trained to grow trees, not ride herd on dudes. By necessity the foresters had to deal reluctantly with aggressive graziers entrenched on the forests. With all these troubles, forest-visiting tourists became a new aggravation to the dedicated tree-growers. A few hardy tourists had visited the forest lands before the first reserves were established. One notable early visitor was a South Dakota rancher named Theodore Roosevelt, who periodically sallied into the highlands now in the Bighorn, Shoshone,

Teton, and other national forests adjacent to them. These early tourists went into the forests by horseback, wagon, buckboard, and the narrow-gauge railways which now are all but vanished from the western mountains. The advent of the automobile and new roads started the boom in tourist travel which continues to bring more and more millions of visitors to the forests.

A few members of the U.S. Forest Service now say bluntly that if the present upward trend in forest recreation continues, this use will soon take precedence over all others. Measured by demands on the time of the Service personnel, this may come to pass. But growing wood and gathering and delivering good water to the streams will still prevail as primary forest objectives—as they should. The recreational use removes nothing material from the land. People can enjoy tree-cloaked mountains and woodland valleys while the growth of the timber and the delivery of water to rivers goes on undiminished.

Recreation is now, at least, the third most important use of the national forests. It is the big bonus value to be enjoyed coincident with growing of wood and protecting water supplies.

We now can more explicitly differentiate the two types of reserved public lands as found in national parks and in national forests. Usually the explanation consists of a statement that the parks are administered by the National Park Service, an agency in the Department of the Interior, while forests are administered by the Forest Service of the Department of Agriculture. Of course, the real difference is more fundamental.

The confusion between parks and forests arises largely from the fact that both consist of extensive wildlands. Also, field men of both parks and forests are called "rangers." The true difference between the two types of properties—so much alike in many features—is found in the services to which they are dedicated.

The primary functions of national forests are material and utilitarian. The national parks are completely directed toward preserving unique examples of typical American landscapes in their natural state. National parks and monuments supposedly are closed to commercial exploitation of the natural resources within them. Because of increasing numbers of visitors, the knottiest of park problems is to provide essential facilities for visitors and at the same time adequately present the parks' unique offerings without damage to those features. By the mid-1950s 50,000,000 people were visiting the parks every year; the impact of numbers on our parks' wildlands treasures is tremendous.

Another difference between parks and forests is that national parks are one-purpose reservations contributing to human knowledge and enjoyment. The national forests, on the other hand, are multi-purpose properties, managed to supply a maximum of material wealth on a sustained-yield basis, as well as to provide enjoyment of outdoor living.

The enjoyment of what is lumped together as "wildlife" could be classed as a part of recreation. It does, however, include material benefits. The taking of game by hunting and fishing supplies delicious meats. With good management these renewable resources can be "cropped" on a sustained-yield basis. In many western localities, especially, hunting and fishing support no small part of a neighborhood's economy.

Attempts have been made to express in dollars the economic worth of hunting and fishing. In a survey I made in 1950 the national average annual expenditure per sportsman for services and goods was indicated as approximately $600. Annual hunting and fishing licenses in recent years have been mounting in numbers sold toward forty million. In 1956 a U.S. Fish and Wildlife Service survey placed the annual sportsmen's spending at $4,000,-000,000; I suspect a tally of all dollars spent because of going hunting or fishing would more than double that figure.

Especially in the west, it would be difficult to reduce to exact statistics the part the forests play in producing a state's game and fish crop. Deer and elk herds generally are on forest lands from early spring to early winter. Deer and antelope must also have key winter range at lower elevations. Bighorns, mountain goats, and Shiras moose may stay in high country the year around. Wildlife experts state that the forests furnish 70 per cent of the habitat requirements of western big-game flocks and herds.

Around 1950 many states abandoned figures in reporting game populations. They now estimate the year-to-year "trend" in the herds. Although hunting seasons have been more liberal in many national-forest areas, an over-all increase continues in many herds of larger game animals. A reduction in one area often is overtopped by increases in another unit.

These estimates made during three decades indicate increases in big-game populations dependent on the national-forest habitat. In 1921 big game on the national forests was reckoned at 585,000 head. In 1931 the estimate was more than doubled to 1,243,000 head. There was an approximate doubling in the next decade when 2,434,000 big-game animals were estimated as dependent on national forests. The 1950 figure was 2,957,000.

By 1955 eleven western states were issuing more than two-and-a-half million hunters' licenses. The same states issued nearly three-and-a-half million fishing licenses that year. The national forests of the west underwrite annual sportsmen business that probably exceeds two billion dollars.

When legislators, sportsmens' clubs, and game and fish departments discuss wildlife, they generally include only species classed as game. There are, of course, other wild residents of the forests: coyotes, magpies, beavers, thrushes, toads, butterflies, serpents, and even insects—all included under the term "wildlife."

Many national forests contain all the values I have listed—wood, watersheds, livestock-grazing, recreation, and the many kinds of wildlife—and provide for their proper uses. One must accept that the forests of the storybooks, with cathedral-like trunks rising to a high-held canopy of leafage, are not ideal for producing wood. In the life of the professional forester, overripe trees are a plaguing problem.

For old wood, like old bones, becomes brittle. Winds get hold of the tops and throw ancient trees into a tangle, which soon becomes half-dead brush and a fire hazard. That tangle also is an ideal incubator for insect pests and fungus diseases. A problem for the forester as timber manager is to put over mature stands to use and establish young trees to take their place.

Species—such as the Douglas fir—that produce seedlings radically intolerant of shade have to be clear-cut; the land must be bared and full sunshine allowed to reach the young trees. Ponderosa pines, whose seedlings prefer shade, can be marked for selective cutting; the oldest trees are felled and an understory of growing replacements rise beside the elders. The cropping plan must fit site and species in any situation.

Along with the growing of wood and watershed protection—the foremost objectives in management—there are the correlative tasks of protecting, producing, and utilizing all the other wealth of the national forests. We now should have a broad outline of why we have national forests and how they contribute to our well-being.

III

THE U.S. Forest Service began its official existence in 1905. For many years those who believed timber must be "farmed" instead of "mined" had striven to have a national system of forests established, but the conservationists were repeatedly thwarted by interests that had grown financially fat through exploitation of natural resources.

Sporadic actions to insure continuing and adequate timber supplies had been undertaken from colonial times. Early sessions of Congress passed laws to protect certain tree species, particularly those needed for merchant and naval vessels; and one of the more earnest attempts to curb the rampant raiding of the timberlands was undertaken by the General Land Office in 1847. By 1851 the clamor of those who were being prevented from converting public timber wealth into personal bank accounts had caused Congress to wreck the G.L.O.'s attempt to safeguard the forests.

Public interest in protecting forests from exploiters was, however, on the increase. The first Arbor Day was celebrated in Nebraska on April 10, 1872. In that year Yellowstone National Park was dedicated as a "pleasuring-ground" for the people. New York created a commission to study wildlands north of the Mohawk River to determine if these should become state-owned. In Maine the legislature adopted a law making land planted to trees tax-exempt for 20 years.

In 1873 Congress passed the "tree claim" act, which allowed a settler to secure title to 160 acres of good prairie land if he agreed to plant a fourth of it to trees.

The American Association for the Advancement of Science met in Portland, Maine, in that year and appointed a committee to draw up memorials to be presented to Congress and the several state legislatures. The association emphasized "the importance of promoting the cultivation of timber and the preservation of forests" and recommended "proper legislation for securing these objectives." Two years later the American Forestry Association was organized. It became a militant force in its demands for adequate laws to protect the nation's timberlands.

The general appropriation act passed by Congress on August 15, 1876, contained an amendment that directed the Commissioner of Agriculture to "appoint a man of approved attainments" to make a general study of the forest resources of the country and report to the Commissioner, who, in turn, should report to Congress. With $2,000 assigned to this purpose, Commissioner of Agriculture Frederick Watts hired Dr. Franklin B. Hough to undertake the study. A first step toward a U.S. Forest Service and the formation of the national-forest system had been taken.

At about this time Carl Schurz, who was both conservationist and politician—he was to become Secretary of the Interior in the cabinet of President Hayes—was urging the establishment of federal forests to be managed in the same way as those he had known in his native Germany.

A Division of Forestry was established in the Department of Agriculture in 1881. It could act only in an advisory capacity, and the field administration of the forests remained a part of the General Land Office.

Dr. Hough completed his studies and submitted his report to the Commissioner of Agriculture in 1883. Two years later New York installed the first state Department of Conservation and created her first forest reserves. Boards of forestry were also authorized in that year in California, Colorado, and Ohio.

These and related events were to become the prologue to the entrance of the U.S. Forest Service as an official conservation agency of government.

Various forward-looking conservation bills introduced in Congress were sidetracked, smothered, and scuttled by those who continued to exploit the nation's resources. But conservationists learned from the experience each time that these raiders upset them by legislative strategies. Finally the conservationists resorted to a favorite move of the opposition and succeeded in launching the national-forest system as a national program.

On March 3, 1891, Congress voted on a general bill revising land laws. To this had been added a rider that allowed the President to establish forest reserves from public domain. The bill and rider became law. When his term ended, President Harrison had signed proclamations that set aside 13,000,000 acres as "forest reserves." There was no provision in the 1891 law for administering these areas; they simply were locked up to have timber in them available at some unspecified future time.

On June 4, 1897, Congress passed the law that opened the forests to use and defined their primary reasons for being. Although amended since in some details, this is the law governing the administration of the national forests today.

Now began the big battle to bring all the timberlands that were in the reserves under scientific and planned management. The General Land Office of the Department of the Interior continued to administer the forest lands. It was a fumbling, half-hearted performance. The Division of Forestry in the Department of Agriculture had a dozen employees—six clerks and six trained scientists. The head of the Division, Gifford Pinchot, wanted field application of forestry principles, but although the Division became the Bureau of Forestry in 1901, it continued to be only an advisory and investigating agency.

Pinchot, his associates, and the American Forestry Association—fortified by Theodore Roosevelt's succession to the Presidency—powered the drive for the transfer of the administration of the forest reserves to the Bureau of Forestry. They were supported by the Secretary of the Interior, Ethan Allen Hitchcock.

On February 1, 1905, Congress passed the act that transferred the forest reserves from the Department of the Interior to the Department of Agriculture. A month later the Agricultural Appropriation Act of 1905 was passed, and the Bureau of Forestry became the U.S. Forest Service. At that time there were 734 employees in the Service, 268 in Washington, D.C., 466 in field service.

The crucial test of whether this progress was to be undercut by greed mixed with political maneuvers began in 1907. Richard A. Ballinger, a former Mayor of Seattle, was appointed Commissioner in the General Land Office. At that time the Secretary of the Interior was James R. Garfield, regarded as an informed and stalwart conservationist.

Ballinger accepted the claim of a Seattle man named Clarence Cunningham to 33 "mining" claims—a total of 5,280 acres—in the Chugach National Forest in Alaska, filed supposedly because of coal deposits on them. Actually there was thousands of dollars worth of prime timber on each claim, which Cunningham hoped to get title to for $10 per claim. If there was any coal on the claims, it was of no material volume.

Beneath official surfaces two opposing armies, the exploiters and the conservationists, locked in a crisis battle. Ballinger was in a position to ram through Cunningham's claims. He did so with four claims that had been sold to a financial syndicate. Then Ballinger left his job as Commissioner in the G.L.O. and immediately became Cunningham's lawyer—contrary to federal law.

In March 1909 William Howard Taft succeeded Theodore Roosevelt as President. Secretary Garfield left office, and Richard Ballinger came back to serve his government and himself as Secretary of the Interior. He now had the whip hand and forced reinstatement of the entries for 14 Cunningham claims. Pinchot resigned as Chief Forester and took this case to the public. The mess was aired on the floors of Congress. Ballinger was exonerated, then resigned, and his name became a symbol of anti-conservation.

Forests were established from the public domain by Presidential proclamation until 1907. In that year western members of Congress succeeded in having a law passed to take away this power as it had been applied in Oregon, Washington, Idaho, Montana, Colorado, and Wyoming; in 1912 California was added to this list. Congress took to itself the authority for creating new forests, and even a change in the exterior boundaries of national forests now must be by act of Congress.

Because the first forests were made up of unreserved and unappropriated public domain, the early "reserves" were established in the west. Practically all of the land east of the Mississippi was first claimed by the states that had been the original colonies. Federal property rights and jurisdictions in the eastern half of the country were conveyed to the nation when the colonies became the United States. When the nation as a whole purchased from Napoleon that vast piece of property known as "Louisiana" there was no question as to who owned the real estate; it was the United States of America. All of the west's great public domain resulted from this, our biggest land deal.

When Thomas Jefferson's gridiron system of land surveys were imposed on all the west, states received by grant an allocation of sections 16 and 36 in each township to underwrite cost of the public schools. Many millions of other acres were conveyed to homesteaders by federal patent.

The forest reserves were composed of better timberlands remaining unappropriated and unreserved in the public domain.

In the east few federal lands were available for "forest reserves"; the state forests in New York had been in existence for a number of years, and other states had established forests.

Before 1910 a militant organization called the Society for Protection of New Hampshire Forests was demanding public ownership of the White Mountains. The slopes of these mountains are most important in collecting waters for the Connecticut River. Floods on that stream can do, and have done, headline-creating damage. This record of flooding was used to press demands for a White Mountain National Forest, which would assist in flood prevention.

In another section of the east, deteriorated watersheds of the Monongahela and the Allegheny poured flood crests on Pittsburgh in 1908, doing $8,000,000 worth of damage. People began to ask where such a flood came from and how it formed. Foresters pointed to bare slopes and told how forests on them could decrease flood dangers. A rising demand for national forests in eastern states brought congressional action.

Three members of Congress have their names rightly commemorated by the forest laws they sponsored. The "Weeks Law" and the "Clarke-McNary Act" are milestones in national-forest chronology.

John Wingate Weeks was a civil engineer and New York banker before he became a congressman in 1905, a Senator in 1913, and a cabinet member under Presidents Harding and Coolidge. Weeks may have had two good reasons for his interest in forestry and the measure that bears his name. First, he was a native of New Hampshire. He need not have had to spend much time in the state's forests, both those ravished and wrecked and others still virgin, without wanting to do something to bring good forestry to his homeland's hills. A second probable reason stems from his service in the House of Representatives while Theodore Roosevelt was President. Both men were Republicans, at that time the party of the conservationists.

The Weeks Law of March 1, 1911, provided for the purchase by the federal government of forest lands that were "necessary to the protection of the flow of Navigable streams."

A few tracts still in the public domain in Alabama, Arkansas, Michigan, Minnesota, and Florida became nuclei of eastern forests. The two forests first set up for purchase were the White Mountain and the Pisgah in North Carolina. Although floods from its slopes spurred passage of the Weeks Law, the Monongahela Forest was not established until 1920.

Charles Linza McNary was born near Salem, Oregon, within view of the great, white, mystic cones of the mountains to the east—Hood, Jefferson, and the Three Sisters.

He became a member of the U.S. Senate in 1917, representing his native state.

In 1924 two groups were locked in contention over various forestry bills in the Congress. The clash occurred between those conservationists—led by Gifford Pinchot—who advocated federal control of forest programs, including private lands, and the owners of those lands, who bitterly opposed such a move. Moreover, Secretary Albert Fall, then head of the Department of the Interior and soon to face downfall in the Teapot Dome oil scandal, was on a rampage to take the U.S. Forest Service out of the Department of Agriculture and move it back to Interior. Conservationists, probably with well-based foreboding, feared a grand-scale sell-out of the forests if Fall should have his way.

In the welter of legislative conflict all bills pushed by forces on either side of this controversy were being lost. It was then that Senator McNary, joining with Congressman John W. Clarke from New York State, shaped what has become known as the Clarke-McNary Act. The Weeks Law had strictly limited purchase of land for the eastern national forests to headwaters of navigable streams. In the Clarke-McNary Law authority was given to purchase lands necessary for the production of timber as well as for the protection of navigable streams, so long as such land was within the basin of such streams. That opened practically any eastern mountain and hill country to purchase by the federal government.

In addition to extending the limits of forest lands to be purchased in the east, by the federal government, this act also provided for fire-protection programs to be carried on co-operatively by states and the federal government. Private owners also could participate in fire prevention and control. This co-operative system, with its pooling of funds and effort, was organized for full-scale fire protection to lands—both privately and publicly owned—in the most important forest areas in the country.

I V

FEDERAL bureaus seem to have more than their quota of semasiologists, who invent official words and phrases. An exasperated Texan named Maury Maverick called the more confusing jargon "gobbledy-gook," and appropriately, that name has been included in most American dictionaries.

A gobbledy-gook term loosely used in relation to the national forests is "multiple use." We must look at it, and do so critically.

Ernest P. Swift, after serving as chief of the Wisconsin wildlife agency and as assistant director of the U.S. Fish and Wildlife Service, became executive director of the National Wildlife Federation. Soon after he joined that organization, Swift offered an illuminating discussion of "multiple use" in the Federation's news bulletin. I quote it as comment from one who in several official capacities has wrestled with the confusing meanings of this seemingly simple term.

"Land managers with specialized training [wrote Swift] are prone to talk multiple-use but continue to practice their own specialty. This can result from early training, personal inclination or the policies they are hired to carry out. There are times when range men, the Soil Conservation Service, and foresters are in competition with each other, and often all three end up in competition with wildlife managers. The ever-increasing demand for forest, range and agricultural land has focused great attention upon ways and means for more effective but specialized land use. . . ."

As Swift then points out, what happens as each specialist makes plans is not a balanced, correlated use of the land and its various values, but a consecutive layering of specialists' schemes with little regard for any co-ordination between them. The sylviculturist lays out his full-scale plan, the range-management specialist superimposes his plan, the wildlife officer operates as if the other uses had to bow to wildlife needs, and the recreational designer throws all these aside as he prepares a program to put human uses ahead of all others. Then some armed-force agency caps the whole layer-on-layer accumulation by demanding the land to test bombs, cannons, or poison gas.

It may not be always as thick, layer on many layers. But often it actually is the specialist with the loudest voice or the highest rating on the civil-service roster who shouts his particular field into first consideration.

In the years when I struggled with the early plans and policies to govern recreation in the national forests, I groped for a better term than multiple use. It should imply that land would be managed with a real priority for the use to which it was best suited. At some point in the groping the term "dominant use" took shape. This term seemed to convey the meaning of an orderly sequence in priorities, beginning with the use of most importance. Nothing new as ideas go, this merely was the application of zoning and city-planning principles to wildlands.

This idea of tying together the graduated and co-ordinated uses in balanced planning and management is probably the most widely accepted interpretation among laymen of "multiple use" in the national forests. But the specialists—often well intentioned—have engaged in this layering of use on use, and somewhat confounded the initial meaning of this term. I still prefer "dominant use" as more accurately implying a process of co-ordinated land-use planning.

To recapitulate the objectives of the national forests are: growing crops of wood, protecting watersheds, grazing of domestic animals, producing wildlife for hunting and fishing, and, finally, providing recreational areas.

Although there are minor variations, you will find these divisions of uses and management fairly well represented in Forest Service organization charts and in government budget-headings, and positively included in the ever-expanding shelf of loose-leaf books called, with reverence or exasperation, "The Manual." This is a collection of directives, legal interpretations, and instructions for every conceivable chore or project in the U.S. Forest Service. Within its covers is to be found the orthodoxy of the U.S.F.S.

When I first encountered The Manual it was one volume smaller than the standard Yearbook of Agriculture. Rangers stuck it in a saddle bag and carried it into the field. Conceivably, a man could read and remember most of what it contained. Now The Manual is a flexible series of loose-leaf books, and no one can forecast at this moment when or where the additions to its text will cease. I do not mean to belittle The Manual; there must be definition and system. But full acquaintance with the forests is achieved only by visiting them—many times.

On these visits you may see the mists of morning, robing the crowns of Washington state's mountains, or trailing skeins of fog, dragging through timber of the lake country. Visiting forests on the dry tablelands of Arizona or New Mexico, you will see the three-toothed sage spreading out mile after mile, like gray-green rugs between the

red-orange boles of old ponderosa pines. In another forest
stand the great, gray ramparts of the Wind River mountains where grinding glaciers give birth to streams milky
with rock flour.

A nodding bluebell above a timberline spring, the sharp
piping of a disturbed marmot, the smell of sun on pine
needles, the cry of a soaring hawk, the crash of ripe old fir as
it is felled, the whine of a little sawmill cutting rough lumber for local ranch buildings, wood smoke, the laughter of
riders on a shadowy trail—all these may be met in the forests. And fire may be encountered, and also the building
of roads and the battles against tiny insects and fungi that
kill trees.

v

ONE main factor that determines the ecological associations in the woodlands of the nation appears to not have
had the recognition that it merits in books concerning national forests. This factor is geology, which, of course, is
the underlying foundation for what exists in the forests.

I always have found something to intrigue me in minor
land forms, a rock fragment, or stratification on a cliff.
But a considerable span of time passed before the full im-
port of the interrelation of major geological formations
and the ecology of the forest abruptly dawned on me. Once
this truth is realized, it insistently demands its place in the
understanding and appreciation of any community of living things within the forest.

Often the mention of geology in books concerning the
national forests is limited to such observations as, for example, that in a specific area the valleys are U-shaped, revealing that they were formed by glaciers; that they are

V-shaped, which indicates streams cutting through the earth mass of a relatively new uplift; or that the terrain is sharp-edged, which means insufficient time has passed for erosion to round off the valley sides. But these again are details and not the full story. Such fascinating details of geological history are by no means to be disregarded; often they reveal larger prospects of earth forms and their relation to forest ecology.

Notch Mountain, which presents such a geological detail, is located in Central Colorado. The notch in its ridge top occurs where a layer of soft rock was caught between masses of harder rock and the whole was heaved skyward. At the same time the layers were tilted to a vertical position. Then erosion scratched the less resistant material out of the Notch. You can stand in the Notch as if in a roofless hallway, and look southward into the chasm where a little lake named The Bowl of Tears nestles, and as your gaze lifts you may see the Christian symbol that has made the Mount of the Holy Cross internationally famous. The standard of the Cross forms when snow has packed into the big trough where the soft rock stratum, continued across the chasm, has sloughed away.

From the top of the Mount of the Holy Cross you can see the north face of Fool's Peak. On the south flank of that mountain, on a blue limestone ledge above the sinkhole where Lost Creek disappears, are fossilized shells of giant snails. Their shapes, pearl-colored, appear in cross-section, for ice has planed and smoothed the blue limestone. And to the west, beyond Glenwood Canyon where the Colorado flows, is the cavern of the South Fork of the White River. It is a strange place, a high-arched vestibule along which you plod through dust up a slight grade to reach a ledge beside a clear, cold, slow-moving stream that blocks further exploration of the cavern.

Questions shape swiftly when you so much as think of
these oddities. The blue limestone ledge, now at an elevation of 10,000 feet, once was clay on the bottom of a very
ancient sea. The cavern of the South Fork was cut by a
river that long ago tunneled and twisted, perhaps as the
massive block of the White River Plateau was shoved upward. Notch and Holy Cross were heaved to almost the
14,000-foot elevation by some writhing of the planet and
now stand as a high, rock-faced baffle that traps the winds,
so that clouds spill their cargoes to water the great spruce
forests spread all across the slopes below timberline.

The national forests, with a few exceptions are associated
with mountains. In Nebraska's sandhills, there is a hand-
planted forest of pines, man-created to demonstrate that
such trees can be grown in the most westerly part of the
state's portion of the Great Plains. National forests along
the coast of the Gulf of Mexico are in natural forest-type
locations typical of southern wetlands. But in practically
every other part of the country, national forests are located where there are or have been mountains.

Immediately you may think of the lake states, of the big
Superior National Forest with its lake-laced wilderness
sanctuary, spreading out between Lake Superior and the
Canadian boundary. There are no mountains—now. But
there were mountains there at one time; the heights of the
Mesabi range once lifted higher than today's Rockies. Then
the glaciers came, knocking the mountains to pieces and
damming the mountain valleys with debris from the
wrecked peaks. The ice in its lowest movements dug deep
to increase the depth of the blue-water lakes that we see today.

Some of the more important reasons why mountains
and national forests are associated are readily apparent.

Unlike the soils of the vanished forest that originally covered our central states, mountain soils are often rocky. Forests were cleared from the sandy loams and fertile clays of Ohio, Illinois, and Iowa so that corn, wheat, timothy, and other crops could be grown. The mountain soils with their rocks were passed by. For this reason the forests retained their mountain homelands. And two of the factors that determine what shall grow on a certain slope or in a certain high valley are the chemical content of that rock-spotted soil and the mountain earth's gravelly open texture that some trees prefer to the tight clays of the lowlands. Physically and chemically, the mountain soils are one of the limiting conditions that determine which plant life shall grow at any certain location.

Climate is another major force that determines the growth of plant life. The mountain slopes of northern Georgia can grow pines twice as rapidly as can the residual ridges of the old Laurentian mountain system far to the north. The length of the growing season, the almost year-round favorable temperature in the Georgia pineries assures rapid growth.

The Mogollon mountains, tumbled about near the line between southern New Mexico and Arizona, have a period of days with favorable growing temperatures nearly as long as that of the Georgia hills. In the southwest, however, the second force governing growth of plants, moisture, determines what vegetation may thrive there. Only those species that accept hot and *dry* locations can live in many parts of the Mogollons, and because of scant moisture, growth is very slow.

Though the overriding patterns that impose weather on the world are beyond modification by mountain heights, the local conditions are not. Moisture evaporated from the Pacific Ocean is freighted eastward on prevailing winds. Rising to higher levels as they move over the coastal and cascade ranges, the clouds release most of their moisture as rain. The big trees of California and the great stands of Sitka spruce and Douglas fir in Oregon and Washington are on the westerly and very moist sides of the mountains. On the eastern, leeward side of the Cascades, on the Wasatch mountains farther east, and on the main Rockies still farther east, plant associations requiring more moisture still are on the Pacific side of main ridges. This is strikingly evident in the neighborhood of Glacier National Park where on the western slopes are fine stands of rain-loving cedars, and on the eastern side the forests are mostly made up of the lodgepole pine and its associates that have adapted themselves to drier sites.

Although the directions from which wind-borne moisture may come are different in other parts of the nation, the pattern that generally applies is that mountains cause rain on the windward side and much less precipitation on the leeward side.

Because the forests are associated with heights still another condition enters into what sort of forest complex may exist at a specific place: the effect altitude has on vegetation. The tops of our higher mountains—the Sierra Nevadas, the Rockies, the Presidential Range—possess the climate of the treeless Arctic. At the foot of Pikes Peak one is in the Upper Sonoran plant association of northern Mexico. *Cholla, mammalaria,* and prickly pear cactus are to be found there. At the top of the peak, a few miles distant, are tiny, fast-blooming, ground-hugging plants, which are also found in tunda country north of the Arctic circle. Climbing from cactus to tundra, one passes through all the zones of typical plant associations, from Albuquerque, New Mexico, to Point Barrows, Alaska.

As the soil, the temperature, and the moisture determine which groupings of plants will grow in specific localities, so the plants add to these conditions their own limitations on what animate life shall be in each locality. The small Arizona white-tail deer and the pigmy mule deer of Sonora are products of the desert. The browse a deer may find there is sparse; the deer must be small or starve. The Shiras moose, which one may see ducking his whole head under water to nose out the roots of the yellow pond lily in a lake in Yellowstone National Park, would not survive in an area where there is not enough chill to wring adequate water from the clouds to allow such ponds and related forage-producing bogs to grow the food plants a moose must have. The prairie dog thrives on the dry cactus and sage flats spreading out from the foot of Pikes Peak while the coney finds habitat to his liking among the treeless meadows and stabilized rock slides atop the famous peak.

Trees are the biggest of the living things within an ecological grouping of a forest. These larger habitants supply clues to all other living things found in their neighborhood, and, using them as a point of beginning, it is possible to work out the long array of all that lives within the local forest community.

Full realization of how positively the geology of a place shapes its ecology usually comes only after one has enjoyed a considerable bit of living in forests. As one might expect, a zoologist, geologist, or botanist might sojourn in a forest area for a while and, becoming engrossed with his specialty, write only of his dominant interest. An ecologist should see the interrelated parts of the woodland and the dependence of plants and animals on each other. But even with this broader point of view, such a scientist may slight the geological factor, which is the foundation on which all this life has developed. In each section devoted to a forest region in this book, moderate attention will be given to earth forms, how they came to pass, and their relationship to the living things encountered in that region.

V I

THE boundaries of the Forest Service "Regions," though drawn primarily for administrative purposes, do outline in a broad way the natural forest regions. Some administrative boundaries encompass several natural regional types, but for the moment let us bypass the geophysical attributes and get fairly acquainted with how the U.S.F.S. is organized to administer the 180,000,000 acres for which it is responsible.

There are nine Regional Offices in continental United States, and one in Alaska. A Regional Office with its divisions and sections presents a fairly typical organization chart which, if considerably expanded, would fit the national headquarters. If trimmed down, the same chart fits the office of a Supervisor of an individual forest. Without following the charts to their last ramification, this is what you will see diagrammed as a representative Regional Office, with Region 5—which is the one state of California—selected as the model.

The top executive of a region is the Regional Forester. He is the so-to-speak "Governor General," responsible to the Chief of the Service in Washington. The Regional Forester has a staff of Assistant Regional Foresters; this staff might be termed as his "Cabinet."

In Region 5, Assistant Regional Foresters are at the head of divisions of Timber Management, Range and Wildlife Management, Recreation and Lands, Fire Control, Engi-

neering, Watershed Management, State and Private Forestry, Operation, Personnel Management, and Information
and Education.

Other important Regional officers are the Fiscal Agent,
the Solicitor (who is the legal counsel), and several "Project
Leaders," such as the scientists heading a drive against
fungus or insect pests. Each division has its staff personnel;
Timber Management, for example, includes those who are
responsible for evaluating timber stands, those who administer timber sales, and others who work on inventory
and management problems related to timber.

As organized in 1959, the Chief of the Forest Service,
with his offices in Washington, D.C., has six Assistant
Chief Foresters on his staff, each heading major divisions of
the agency's activities. Other divisions, with their respec-
tive directors, deal with such subjects as finance and budget,
administrative management, and various services to personnel and the public.

Responsibility in the U.S. Forest Service follows a direct
line. Timber management is a major division in each
region; also in the Washington office. The Regional division head is responsible to the Regional Forester; in the national headquarters the head of Timber Management is
responsible to the Chief. The Regional Forester is individ-
ually responsible to the Chief for all that happens in his
region.

The Supervisor of a forest is responsible to the Regional
Forester. He may have three, four, a half-dozen Assistant
Supervisors working out of his office. Finally, right out at
the earthy level where trees grow, fires blaze, water falls,
and wildlife romps, there is the Ranger District, the ultimate subdivision calling for Forest Service staffing. And
the Ranger, with an assistant or two, is responsible to the
Supervisor.

The title "ranger" has about it an air of adventure. Though there is undoubted glamour and true adventuring of sorts in a ranger's work, for the most part his job is plain work and much of it. Anyone in a green uniform and wearing the bronze badge of the Forest Service has, at one time or another, been addressed as "Ranger." The man who rates that title is in charge of a District and is on the front line of action in every field job within the national forests. Should one make a mistake and address any other member of the Forest Service as "Ranger," it should cause no such embarrassment as would, for example, addressing an Army colonel as "Sergeant." In their time, and including all those who have been Chiefs of the Service in recent years, practically every higher official in the U.S.F.S. has been a ranger. It is a proud title in the Forest Service.

Being a ranger is no small job. A typical western district will contain from 250,000 to 350,000 acres. If each acre is worth as little as $5 to $10, the ranger manages property containing several million dollars in basic wealth. Of all the distorted ideas of what a ranger is and what he does, the one that envisions him as being on a perpetual hunting-and-fishing spree is the silliest. A ranger works, putting all his skill and know-how into each action and decision. He is responsible, after all, for what happens to public property worth from a few million to several hundred million dollars.

Regional boundaries often disregard state lines in the organization of the ten regions of the U.S. Forest Service. Such a situation exists in Washington state. East of the Cascade Mountains lies a wide stretch of flat and rolling country. This contains Washington's wheat belt and her cattle ranches. In the northeastern quarter of the state, however, is an extension of the main mountain systems of northwestern Montana and northern Idaho. These contain masses of high country and forests. Though Portland is headquarters for Region 6, which includes most of Washington, it is easier to administrate the forest operations of extreme eastern Washington from Missoula, Montana, Region 1 headquarters, than from Region 6. That northeastern corner of Washington is part of Region 1.

Travel facilities between headquarters and forests, and also between forests, had some bearing on regional boundaries. Railways were the principal means of getting about a region when I first journeyed to and through forests of Region 2. One trip regional officials often made consisted of boarding a Pullman car in Denver after sundown and arriving the following afternoon in Cody, Wyoming, headquarters of the Shoshone National Forest. In that evening only about enough time remained to plan field travel for the next day. The next leg of the trip was by automobile along unpaved roads, or by horse out along trails. There were and still are more miles of trails in the national forests than of highways: about 145,000 miles of trails to 124,000 miles of roads. But today there are genuine motorcar highways through the forests rather than the old wagon roads the early autoists had to negotiate.

The time required to rush fire-fighting equipment from the regional headquarters always was important. The region's shape was affected somewhat by fire-control plans. Whenever state lines fitted in with other needs they were selected as regional boundaries, but only if they thus conformed.

A recent map shows the Forest Service regions. In a considerable degree these also bound nature's forest-type regions. Chiefs of the Forest Service undoubtedly recognized the value of putting forests with reasonably similar composition in charge of one Regional Forester and his staff, another major forest type in custody of another man and staff. Problems similar throughout a region thus would have more experienced and consistent administration.

VII

A STRANGE thing happens when I think of the various regions. They are not areas marked out on a map, nor even sweeping, wide-flung lands on which plant groupings are relatively the same. In my odd way of remembering, a mental tour of the whole northeastern region begins with the song of a whippoorwill.

We had driven across the winter-browned prairies, past the old tree claims where cottonwood leaves were breaking from winter shells, and into the corn belt. East of the Mississippi we saw the still-leafless elms of various shapes: the urns, fans, vases, and oak types. They stood high on little knolls where white buildings of Illinois farmsteads seemed still to drowse as spring came softly to mid-America.

On the prairies where a pitiful few patches of virgin sod had escaped the cult of clean cultivation, little star flowers, the earliest of grassland's posies, had been in bloom. As we came to the Alleghenies all the woodlands were turgid with spring. Only a few hours of sunny time would precipitate the miracle of leaves exploding from twigs that were bare the night before, and the flowering shrubs would be soon cloudy bouquets on the hillsides.

We stopped one night near a Pennyslvania village in one of those early day "cabin camps," furnished with austere iron beds and hard-felted mattresses, forerunners of today's lush-and-plush motels. The woods were close by this place; actually they had crept back into the "tourist court" grounds after the builder had cleared the area.

Dusk came. A feeling of restlessness persuaded us to follow a very old woods road that led away from the cabins. A medley of sounds mixed through the growing dusk. Birds of the daylight hours, unseen in the darkling woods, were making sleepy talk. In the valley, beyond the half-naked black cherry, birch, ash, and maple trees, cattle lowed. In another direction toads shrilled.

As if it were a shuttle lacing together all that was of the place and the moment, we heard the song of the whippoorwill. Over and over and over the same plaint sounded, sad, sweet, and full of compulsion. Compulsion was there, for although we heard the song as mournful, it was the bird's ecstatic mating-call.

The rounded tops of the old mountains, the soft air (so in contrast with that of the dry-farming belt we had crossed just east of Denver), the hardwood trees, and the smell of the moist leaf mold mixed now and then with a bit of woodsmoke and perhaps no more than an imagined bit of wildflower perfume—all these trooping recollections come to me as I remember the bird song one evening when spring was arriving in the Alleghenys.

There are other recollections of the northeastern forests: one is of late autumn days when the hill country of southern Vermont was brown; another of a day in the Allegheny National Forest when every ridge and dingle throbbed with vivid, mixed color.

Those are recollections that race by as I look at the map produced by the General Printing Office of the United States. Add to these landscapes of the memories the great domed tops of the Virginia mountains as seen first from a smoke-tainted troop train during World War I, the spiky cedars, the tangling cat briar of the Shenandoah country. For me, these sketch the countenance of Region 7, the eastern region, which lies northward of the southern borders of Kentucky and Virginia and eastward of the river and state both named Ohio.

Region 8 (which includes all the states east of Texas and Oklahoma to the Atlantic), also has its identifying memory. The plume-like young pines creeping back to reclaim abandoned and eroded fields of northern Georgia, the oaks still standing which saw the surge of war between the states, the mistletoe in the great trees spreading above tired, gray clapboard cabins sitting on stilts—these belong to Region 8. The pines and the mills that were ripping sawlogs into lumber in the country between Longview and Marshall, Texas, is another remembered scene. Then there is the country of western Arkansas, near Mena, within the Ouachita, oddly pronounced "Wash-e-taw," with greenery of the hickories, the oaks, the elms over the hills.

So it is with the other regions. For me, each has some identifying "tag." Loon song at dusk as moose cows brought new calves into the world on island-strewn Lake Insula in northern Minnesota identifies Region 9 (the north-central region, which includes the "Lake States" and also the Ozark country). In Region 1 (Montana) I remember the myriads of lodgepole pine trees, growing straight where fires swept the mountains in 1910. There are trooping memories of Region 2 (the mid-Rockies) that typify these lands, this region, and its living residents both animal and vegetable. They include sunlight filtering through half-grown aspen leaves to wash with thin gold the floor of a little valley of the Spanish Peaks country where a very heavy-bodied old lady porcupine waddled frantically toward some hiding-place. There was another hour when I stood at the tip of the Mount of the Holy Cross, gazing over the highest, smashing mid-section of the Rockies or looking down that gash in the rock where collected snow forms the standard of the Cross.

The southwestern region (Region 3, New Mexico and Arizona) brings up a scene of dryish uplands where very old ponderosa pines rear high. Or beyond the cactus and the shimmer of sun-blasted terrain, you see mountains jabbing skyward and their sides timbered and green and inviting. The intermountain Region (the Great Basin area of Utah, Nevada, and southern Idaho, Region 4), is typified by hours spent leisurely traversing a truck trail through the Fishlake National Forest of southern Utah, or the massive upthrust of the Wasatch Mountains, culminating in Mountain Tympanogos, or the wild lands of the Salmon River country in Idaho.

Region 6 (the Pacific northwest)—there can be no question of what is thought of as typifying Region 6— brings to mind the tremendous, twigless boles of the giant Douglas firs, the patches of pure-stand cedars, the shadowland beneath the mighty trees all mossy and full crowded with ferns. But outside these forests, are vistas of patches of forest, back-drops for the fertile farms in the Willamette valley.

From Region 5, which is the only one containing but a single state, California, there are great, burry cones resting beside our living-room fireplace—and I remember the day we halted the car as we drove from Carson City to Lake Tahoe, and picked up these foot-long sugar pine cones that had rolled down the slope to where they would be crushed by traffic if left ungathered. Beyond that moment are the blue waters of Tahoe, the smashing east face of Mount Whitney, the big trees on the westerly side of the Sierra Nevada, the "brush forest" of California's most southerly forest, the Cleveland, where the wild lilac blooms. Some larger trees are found on the Cleveland, but most of the cover of the slopes is bush, and the all-important business of this forest is to protect watersheds.

These are the regions in the states. Far northward, along Alaska's southern coasts, are the great virgin timber stands of the new state. Those forests, the Tongass and the Chugach, are Region 10.

The *natural* forest regions of the nation, as opposed to administrative regions, are those broader types of landscape where similar climate, earth forms, and soil types combine to support reasonably similar associations of plants, animals, and insects.

Henry Solon Graves, an early associate of Pinchot, pioneered at Yale when that university offered the first degree in forestry, later became Chief Forester of the U.S., and in 1899 wrote *Practical Forestry in the Adirondacks*. He is credited with having applied the term "forest type" to a typical association of trees, and with them all other denizens of the grouping, and the term has had continued acceptance.

Controversy still exists as to where the lines should be drawn to bound natural "forest-type" regions. In part this is because there are so many tree species in the country, about four times as many as in Europe. Tree species do get mixed together when so many kinds compete for living space. But if we accept a recent Forest Service map which outlines the natural forest types by lines and dots, there is a grand halving of the nation between types east of the Mississippi and those west of the river. There are nine types east, the same number west—a total of eighteen.

There are nine Forest Service administrative regions. This merely means we will find more than one forest-type region in some of the U.S. Forest Service administrative regions. Whether or not a block of hilly country should be divided into several units or can be classified as one type depends somewhat on how little you believe may be required to differentiate one plant-animal community from another. One scientist will call a score of valleys, peaks, and ridges a single ecological unit; another will divide it into several.

Knowing the regional system of administration the Forest Service has adopted may help in knowing the forests. At least in a broad way the administrative regions are also general type regions. But I suspect you will remember not boundary lines but the yearning call of the whippoorwills, the old white pines of the lake states with their needles so thready the tree crowns look almost like clouds against a red sunset, and the smash and crash of thunderstorms cannonading among the massive peaks of the Neversummer Mountains. For if you harvest such moments, you learn that you are a part of this living world—that in these forests there is more than wood, or venison, or water pouring to power plants, or beef and hides and wool and mutton.

II

MEET REGION 7

I

By ANY everyday measure of time a piece of cliff in the
Franconia Notch of New Hampshire's White Mountains
must be regarded as ancient. I first saw the outline of this
profile rock, The Old Man of the Mountains, illustrated by
a fuzzy line-drawing reproduced in a paperbound booklet
published by The Youth's Companion. It became for me,
as it has for many, a symbol of great age; if The Youth's
Companion approved the word "Old" in its name, that
picture rock had to be ancient.

In 1915 the Old Man rock was threatened. Seepage, frost,
and heat had worked loose a large chunk of one of five
ledges that form the 40-foot silhouette. The Great Stone
Face was going to crack up? Unthinkable!

Nathaniel Hall discovered this rock oddity in 1805 while
hunting partridges, and led his associates to see it. It became a landmark and a tourist lodestone. To preserve it,
the profile was fitted with a set of steel rods that will prevent the Old Man of the Mountains from falling apart.

I shall use the rock profile as a starting-point as we begin
exploring the U.S. Forest Service's Region 7. This region is
the one that includes the White and Green Mountains of
New England and the several national forests in the Appalachian system, running southward to the boundaries
between the Virginias and North Carolina. Thus it in-

cludes the Shenandoah Valley and the Blue Ridge Mountains.

The Old Man of the Mountains is a good starting-point, because this famous rock formation also relates to geology and the whole massive, intriguing, challenging story of how the earth was shaped into the hills where national forests of Region 7 now grow.

We think of the Old Man's great antiquity. But if we are to probe into the long-gone, the really old yesterdays of the forests of Region 7, we have to go eons on eons back, long, long before this very modern rock picture formed, though it is at present saved from senile deterioration only by applying the face-saving touch with steel bands and rods.

We have to go 'way, 'way back to days long before Franconia Notch formed, to understand what we see in the hills and their forests in Region 7.

II

No HUMAN being saw the dawn of the day when volcanoes smoked and roared where the waters of the gulf of Maine now roll. For quite a period the throats of those mountains belched cinders and ash. Ripping winds, high-shooting drafts carried the dust from the earth's forges to high levels. Gentler airs then took it to where New Hampshire's White Mountains now stand.

In the years when those winds blew there was not even the stone nub of an earth wrinkle where New England's highest mountains, Washington, Jefferson, Madison, and Tripyramid now rear their heads. A shallow, lazy sea that sometimes writhed beneath hurricanes such as man never has seen spread above that segment of our hemisphere.

Scrap from those old volcanoes sifted down, falling softly, like a black, mineralized snow, to form a dark layer of cindery mud on the prehistoric ocean's floor.

The ocean's arm spreading between the volcanoes and the mainland extended southwesterly, across earth surface that we know as Pennsylvania, the Virginias, and the Carolinas. That ancient rocky land that once stood east of the lagoon bears the name of "Appalachia" in geological geography.

All of this Appalachia, a subcontinent, or perhaps more accurately an island, was a stark, barren, bulged-up chunk of earth flux—greater than any island we now have off shore on either coast. Weather with many moods, most of them violent, slashed at the rocks of Appalachia. Sands and gravels found in or near the southernmost national forests in Region 7 were washed from this vanished land and spread on the floor of the brackish slough.

This tremendous lagoon was open at both ends. Waters that moved in laggard sympathy with the sea must have aided in the even layering of those dust showers that had been blown sky-high from volcanoes and the sands washed from stony hills. Layer on layer these primitive earths were spread over the muddy sea bottom. Under the spell of the ages it finally became water-formed rock.

Some geologists reckon that the great lagoon and the rocky land mass of Appalachia were in existence 500,000,-000 years ago.

After the stratified mud became sedimentary rock, more time passed, perhaps as much as 250,000,000 years. In all this time there was no period when waters and rock and what we call soil remained static. Always there was struggle—the travail of the planet progressing toward human occupancy. After centuries of lesser writhings a major movement of earth crust began. The earth's rind began to wrinkle and fold. Pressures and torques built up beyond our comprehension. Terrific heat was generated.

That heat was so fierce that rocks became plastic. They bent as one would bend the side of a rubber overshoe. Heat and pressure changed the rock that had been volcanic dust, then mud, then soft, sedimentary stone. The water-laid stone was made more dense but it retained the layers— and as you now look at the flint-hard, gneisses and schists that are the outstanding rocks of the Presidential Range in the White Mountains, you see the layers in what geologists term a metamorphosed state, seams in a changed, heat-fused, pressure-folded rock.

All along the segment of the globe where nearer portions of the Atlantic Ocean now roll, but where the bare, hard, primitive land mass stood, these stresses became active. They performed great feats in changing what had been dust and mud to tight-textured stone, but their great and spectacular act was the cracking of the earth crust. Molten stone squeezed up through these cracks and then, cooling, became the core of great mountain peaks. Even if a man had been there, he would never have seen but a fragment of this great performance. It took hundreds of thousands of years for those plugs of core rock to ooze up through the cracks of earth's shell, and they did not then exude above the surface. There was a mantle of other earth crust above the mushy plugs. Once they cooled the plugs hardened to supply us with our finest granites.

The mountains that rose were high. How high is a question. But in the many centuries of up-wrinkling which followed this first folding, some authorities estimate the mountains rose a total of two miles above the sea. Their crests were never at that altitude at any one time. Rain, wind, frost, heat slashed and clawed constantly as the mountain masses rose, always in a race to see which could

act faster, the rise of the hills or the forces tearing them
down.

At least once, so the stone-readers tell us, these great
mountains of our eastern-seaboard country were whittled
down to nearly a flat plain. Then there was an encore of the
constructive cataclysms: the heaving and twisting, the
burbling and spouting of lava fountains, the roaring of
volcanoes, and again the atmosphere was thick with fine
dust of evolution and turmoil. Again the underlying rocks
became hot, soft, and runny; again the earth's stone case
cracked, and the basic rock squirted up through the cracks
—that "squirting" progressing so slowly it spent centuries
in slow motion.

When the violence of this second upheaval did subside,
two great typographic features of our eastern states were
much in the general form and location they are today. In
New England the White, Green, and Taconic Mountains
were established. From their location, all the distance
down to the southern part of our Forest Service's Region 7,
the other ridges and high points of the Appalachian
mountains were cast in approximately their present shape.
A great thrust of very old earth crust, a slip, an overriding
sheet that was shattered in the movement slid westward
and became the upper measures of all the mountains in
this great system. Some experts have estimated that there
was as much as 50 miles traversed in the overslip of this
plate of earth crust.

The thrust as well as the upward squeeze of core rock
produced the second great land form of Region 7: the Appalachian Trough. The depression where the tremendous
lagoon had spread its shallow waters was lifted above sea
level to become a gigantic valley. It is not a continuous
valley, for it is laced by lesser land forms. A "trough" between mountains is a better term, and if you were able to

rise to sufficient height, somewhere in the neighborhood of Gallopolis, Ohio, and could see clearly land forms from Maine to North Carolina, you'd see the mountains of the Appalachian system and the existence of the Trough between the higher land on either side of it.

There still was one great act of earth-shaping to come and leave its touch on the northern mountains of Region 7 —the White, Green, and Taconic masses. This next earth-carving occurred in what is called the "Ice Age." We say that glibly, not realizing that our presently known racial history, as puzzled out by archaeologists, has happened in this age. Today's polar caps, the continental glaciers, are phenomena of the Ice Age. We still are in a phase of this age; we are creatures of it and its climate.

III

In some indefinite century between 1,000,000 and 500,000 years ago snow began to stack up in northern Canada faster than it melted. A great snow mountain formed. The pressure fused snow into ice. It piled so high that the lower edges began to push out as a sheet of ice in all directions.

The ice sheet, with the squeeze-pressure behind it, spread over ridges and down into valleys. It climbed high peaks, then cascaded over the farther sides, gouging and digging and shoving. This great mass of solidified water would retreat in some centuries, advance again, retreat and advance in irregular sequences. In its farthest push southward it never reached the mountains in Kentucky and the Virginias, where our Monongahela, George Washington,

Jefferson, Shenandoah, and Cumberland National Forests are located. But in the White and adjacent mountains grinding, sliding, rock-bitted glaciers at one time or another covered every part of the giant hills.

Until a few years ago it was believed that the upper 500 feet of Mount Washington and similar elevations on adjacent mountains had not been covered by the ice. Then, digging for the footings of a radio tower, workers found a sticky clay, some transported rock, that could have been deposited at the top of New England's highest peak only by the high-riding sheets of ice. These materials were identical with those found in other, lower-level formations which were proven to be ice-carried.

The final contours of today's major earth forms and formations in the Green Mountain and White Mountain National Forests were shaped by glacial ice. This was "recent"; some of this occurred as late as only 25,000 years ago.

In the more southerly forests of Region 7 you will find what is left of very old mountains worn down and chiseled by those forces described by the term erosion. The core rock of the Blue Ridge and Great Smoky Mountains is so old that there are no fossils in it. This is rock of the Pre-Cambrian era. At one or more times the peaks and ridges may have been as high as the present-day Rockies, as stark and bitter-bitten as the Kofa or Cabeza Parieta ranges that stand ragged and naked above a desert peneplain east from Yuma, Arizona. Here in the southern Appalachians we find the same heat-and-torsion type of stone that was finally made of the muds laid down by volcanic dust in the White Mountain area. But here there was no such ice-scouring process as the one that shaped final forms of the northern Appalachian heights. The southern divisions of mountains that run through our eastern states are good and accepted examples of ancient, unglaciated mountains.

High on shoulders of mountains in the Presidential Range are rocks carried there by moving ice. There also are great scratches 12 feet long and ¼ inch deep on ledges at the head wall of Tuckerman Ravine. Both are evidence of recent ice work. These details are snow-covered when troops of skiers visit Tuckerman. But in any season you can't miss the shape of that valley at Tuckerman; only an alpine glacier could have dug this cirque and the others near by.

Notice on the maps or as you travel that the "notches" of these northern mountains run all the way through the big hills. They are not valleys excavated by streams. They are open at both ends. There may have been a beginning of a defile where these now exist, but it was finally a "deep current" of the continental ice sheet, a sort of low-thrusting ice fin—perhaps well bitted with hard rocks—which plowed out a softer stratum of rock to shape these "notches."

We can continue to think of the Old Man of the Mountains as old, though in truth, the Great Stone Face of Franconia is very young. It has been there not much longer than the retreat 25,000 years ago of the most recent ice invasion of what is now the White Mountain National Forest.

I V

THE heights, dells, and woodlands of the White Mountain National Forest are more intensively used for recreation than any similar public property. Soon after the Revo-

lutionary War Reverend Abel Crawford built the house
that bears his family's name in the Notch and began to
offer accommodations to travelers. He established the first
"resort" in the area, and it has been a vacationists' mecca
ever since.

At least five north-south highways follow the "notches"
through the White Mountains. Along these old routes are
splashes of Indian lore and some well-aged history of Eu-
ropeans and their progeny. Many Indian names have persisted. Mt. Chocorua, for example, was named for the chief
whose son ate poisoned food that one Cornelius Campbell
had set out as bait for a fox. The little Indian died. Chocorua waited until Campbell was away from home and then
killed Mrs. Campbell and the children. A few days later
Campbell caught up with the Indian as the latter stood
near the edge of a cliff. Reportedly, Campbell commanded
Chocorua to jump, the Indian refused, and Campbell shot
him forthwith. The mountain is the chief's memorial.

Pequawket, Pemigewasset, and Ammonoosuc are Indian
names; search a little on the map of the White Mountain
National Forest and you'll find these and a few other
names given by the Indians to their landmarks. Here the
word "wigwam" was used by the Penobscot branch of the
Abnakis to denote their wicker houses; the word came to
mean almost any shelter used by any Indian tribe. If you
do search a forest map, look for a little brook between the
Presidential and Dartmouth ranges, near the head of the
Crawford Notch. Here the tribal name is spelled "Abenaki."
With the proud Presidentials on one side and Dartmouth
on the other, here is a reminder of the whole race of town-
dwelling, crop-growing Indians who called the White
Mountains their country before white-skinned invaders appropriated the land.

Names given to places are often ordinary. In the White

Mountains we'll find Lookout, Iron, North, South, Middle, and Haystack Mountains; Swift, Wild, Mad, Rocky, Beaver, and Dry rivers or brooks. We need never to feel we are in a strange land with such names; halt in any national forest throughout the east, north, and west and ask the whereabouts of Beaver, or Dry Creek, Haystack, or Lookout Mountain, and you will be told where they lie, for these are the common place names of America.

A constant and beguiling invitation to pathways branching from main travel lines is a fault, or a virtue, of national forests. I venture we find more of what we may wish to see and hear and touch along the less trod ways than in the vehicular torrents on the highways. Although it is one of the more traveled thoroughfares, natural and man made, through the White Mountains, let us follow U.S. 3 northward through Blair and toward Littleton, which lies beyond Franconia Notch.

Stop a little while at Campton and visit the U.S. Forest Service's Campton Pond Recreation Area above the "Upper Village." A 40-acre pond, a 1200-foot-long beach, bathhouse facilities, fireplaces, tables, and places to pitch camp are available.

The national forests in 1959 contained 4,900 camp grounds and picnic sites capable of serving 40,000 families at any one time. Such rules as apply on these areas are to protect them. Small fees, if any, that are charged for use of the facilities aid in maintaining the property.

Heading on up the Notch, a very short side road leads to The Flume, a famous defile through which rush waters of Flume Brook. A little farther along, as you have traversed and almost come out of Franconia Notch, is the right spot to pause, look up at the mountain to the southwest of the highway, and see The Profile, The Great Stone Face, or The Old Man of the Mountains. I wonder if the

Indians had a name for the hard-featured silhouette, or ever noticed it!

Another road, U.S. 302, running northward from the town of Conway, nearly bisects the forest. Plan for time to visit the Bartlett Experimental Forest at the village of Bartlett. Here, since 1931 the Forest Service has been studying what can be done in the management of 2,600 acres which are representative of some 8,000,000 acres of northern hardwood forests in Maine, New Hampshire, Vermont, and western Massachusetts. What may be found as good procedure, or bad, on the Bartlett plots can point the way to best handling of the other forest acres.

The experimental area was first logged commercially in 1870. Other waves of logging followed, each taking out the best remaining trees. Spruce went in the first drive, then yellow birch and sugar maple. What was left finally was similar to many other forest stands that were worked in similar patterns. Most of the remaining older trees of good species were defective, not worth the cutting. The younger stock and the sound older trees were species of less value to lumbermen. Beech, less valuable than spruce, pine, maple, or yellow birch, became dominant in places where other trees had been cut. Here, also, are abandoned fields of farms that "wore out" when cultivated. Records are kept of how the forest sends in its advance guard and follow-up troops of young trees to recapture the "worn-out" land. Also the preservation of a few plots where no cutting will be done at all, places where natural forces rule undisturbed, serves as a check against which "managed" areas can be compared.

And finally here is a representative section of land on which young men who elect to follow the profession of forester can find within a limited space, and observe for themselves, the results of various methods of handling the hardwood forest of the northeastern states—a school out-doors, a clinic for students and practitioners alike.

Near by and throughout the White Mountain National Forest, for many years still to be recorded, the marks of a great storm can be seen. During the hurricane of September 21, 1938, 110,000 acres of timber were blown down. Estimates place the total blowdown at 200,000,000 board feet of timber with only some 80,000,000 board feet of sufficient size and accessibility to permit being salvaged. A very serious fire hazard was created by the storm-thrown timber as it died and dried. However, because of fire-prevention programs, official vigilance, the climate which is more moist than some of the greater fire areas of the western forests, and perhaps above all, the caution of the people who came to the forest and enjoyed it, there were no serious fires for a dozen and a half years following the storm. Before the clean-up was completed, 270 transactions led to almost 100 per cent of the wind-thrown timber being used.

Ahead on U.S. Highway 302 is Crawford Notch, the ice-routed corridor discovered by Timothy Nash in 1771 as he pursued a moose. However, let us swing back to take another route from Conway.

Traveling on U.S. 302 from Conway, turn onto State Highway 16, to pass the Thorn Mountain and Black Mountain ski areas. Traversing Pinkham Notch, passing Glen House, you come to the Dolly Copp Forest Camp. If you wish, by all means interrupt your travel to follow the toll road from Glen House to the top of Mount Washington. You can also reach the top by that very famous cog railroad on the other side of the mountain. But don't overlook Dolly Copp and the campground named after that strong-minded woman.

Dolly was the hard-working wife of a pioneer farmer.

The couple had struggled to a point where they had a fair farm wrested from the wilderness. Finally Dolly had enough of living with one man in one place for so long a time. One day she walked away from the house, never to return.

This Dolly Copp campground has developed into one of the best organized public-forest camping-centers in the country. As many as 35,000 man-days of camping per season are provided by this campground. Many of those who come are repeat visitors. These regular visitors have elected their own set of "municipal" officers—an entirely unofficial "mayor," with town board and other members of a village staff.

Officially, the famous Appalachian Club operates both the Dolly Copp and the Campton campgrounds. A small charge is made for camping. A party may stay fifteen days, then it may be required to move on unless there is no demand for space. The Dolly Copp campground is one hub from which the trails into the high country lead to the peaks of the near-by Presidential and Carter ranges. A great network of trails beyond these can be followed to every corner of the forest.

There is much to persuade one to linger long in the White Mountain National Forest and travel its many trails and highways. For this New England forest offers 100 miles of Forest Service roads, 800 miles of trails, and contains some 722,000 acres. It has 18 camp-picnic areas, 39 lakes, 650 miles of fishable streams. It produces 15-20,000,000 board feet of timber yearly with a value of $180,000. From precipitation gathered within the basins cradled in the big hills water flows to 71 communities with a population of 85,000 people.

The famous weather station on Mount Washington, 6,288 feet above sea level and the highest point of land in New England, attracts many visitors. Amateur ornithologists may see robins, phoebes, orioles, a troop of warblers, a squad of sparrows (of the kinds that sing), finches, swallows, wrens, and many other species of birds in the woodlands of the White and Green mountains. White-tail deer will stand immobile in forest shadows and allow you to pass unaware of their nearness, or race away snorting lustily and flashing the white flag that is so characteristic of all the white-tail deer in a hurry.

Together the White Mountain National Forest and the Green Mountain National Forest contain nearly 600,000 acres of fascinating country splashed with bright history and full of crannies packed with beauty. We have merely touched on the gentle beauty and massive grandeur these forests offer.

V

MOVING now to the more southerly forests of Region 7 we shall halt enroute briefly at the Allegheny National Forest in northwestern Pennsylvania. In this sort of country we listened to the whippoorwill. Then one autumn day we motored easterly from Sharon through the Allegheny forest.

The Allegheny forest, established in 1923, is about 37 miles long, 43 miles wide, its northern boundary coincident with that of Pennsylvania and New York, its southern boundary the Clarion River. It contains about 750,000 acres. Close to 500,000 of these are owned by the United States. Improved picnic-camping-swimming areas have been established. Several organizations, Boy Scouts, Y.M.C.A., Girl Scouts, and others maintain summer camps on this forest under special use permits.

The forest contains 500 miles of trout streams. Approximately 50,000 hunters visit the forest during deer season, for, as in most of the national forests, hunting is permitted under state laws and regulations.

Drainage from this forest is mostly westward, to the Ohio River. The topography is a rolling upland, a relatively young peneplain, with its streams in deep, sharp valleys. The low point in the forest at Tionesta has an elevation of 1,064; the high point is approximately 2,200 above sea level near Kane. There is a small patch of glaciation in the northwest corner of the forest; the other soils are residual. These are typical "hardwood soils," deep clay loam, grayish color, acid, rather cold, somewhat leached, and supplied with good humus in the upper layer. They are underlaid by sandstone, some shale, and conglomerates —the old ocean-bed formations similar to structures found in the Ohio valley.

In 1749 Captain Celoron de Plainville floated down the Conewango River in a canoe. He left behind an inscribed lead plate declaring that this land belonged to the King of France. The Supervisor's office is located in Warren, which was founded in 1795 and named for General Joseph Warren, who was killed at Bunker Hill. Laid out by General William Irvine and Andred Ellicott for the Holland Land Company, Warren's first structure was a blockhouse. One of the earliest activities at Warren was staking timber claims. The good timber was cut off, the claim then abandoned, and the process was repeated on another claim. The logs were floated in "Broadhorn" rafts all the way from Warren to New Orleans.

Today there are some 23 economically important tree species in the Allegheny forest. Each year 15 larger sawmills produce 43,000,000 board feet of timber, 31 smaller plants saw out 16,100,000 board feet, and 8 plants use 15,000,000 board feet of timber for distillation processes. Some of the special wood products from the Allegheny forest are boot and shoe lasts, bowling-pins, baskets, boxes, tool handles, barrel staves, and baseball bats. With such an array of wood uses, nobody can say timber business is gone from western Pennsylvania.

Near the forest's center is the Tionesta area, purchased by the U.S. Forest Service from the Central Pennsylvania Lumber Company. It is as near a "virgin" forest as can be found in these hills, containing both hemlock and hardwood timber that have never been logged commercially.

A better-known natural area is located near Warren, Pennsylvania. It contains one of the few untouched stands of white pine and hemlock representative of the original eastern forests. It is worthy of special note that those who first proposed this bit of forest as a natural woodland sanctuary were officials of the Wheeler & Dusenbury Lumber Company. The tract as it is now constituted was completed by the Federated Women's Clubs of Pennsylvania —which matched the 20-acre gift of the lumber company—and by the purchase of 100 acres by the federal government. This forest sanctuary is called "Hearts Content."

V I

The George Washington, Jefferson, Monongahela, and Cumberland, the four southern forests in Region 7, are located in Virginia, West Virginia, and Kentucky. They are rich in color and opportunities for outdoor living.

Here, in the southern Appalachians, is found some of the oldest rock on the earth. Here too one may see more readily the stupendous rippling of our planet's skin, the squeezing and slipping and faulting that lifted the rocky ridges and, along with these upheavings, formed the Appalachian

Trough. It was no pigmy effort that elevated the floor of that lagoon, which was 200 to 300 miles wide and 2,000 miles long, so the emerged land became a colossal valley floor. How high the ridges lifted on either side of that trough is not too certain; one estimate is that the uplift totaled 20,000 to 30,000 feet. The thrust was never so high at any one period, but at times the ridges may have stood higher than our present-day Rockies.

We know the rise of these mountain masses of Region 7's southern forests was slow because of the way today's rivers flow; we know there were not even local glaciers in this part of the continent, for the valleys are V-shaped, showing they are stream cut. Here is the proof of the slowness of the rise of the mountains. North of the Roanoke River the streams originate *west* of the highest ridge, but flow eastward through gorges or gaps the stream continued to cut as the earth crust rose. South of the Roanoke headwaters of the streams are *east* of the highest ridge, but flow westerly through stream-cut gaps. So the land rose deliberately, and the streams persisted in following their established courses, scouring channels deeper as land blocks rose.

History is deep layered in and around Region 7's southern forests. General Washington had planned to use Virginia's Fort Valley, located in the northeasterly division of the George Washington National Forest, as a last-stand fastness in case colonial troops were driven to such an extreme by the British. Access to the Valley is through Passage Creek Gorge, a spot of natural defensive formations. Less-known battlefields of the Revolution are close by or within these forests, and some of the most decisive engagements of that war took place on them.

No less revered are the hundreds of shrines linked with the days when brave men fought under the gallant Stars

and Bars of the Confederacy and others followed the flag
of the Union. Lynchburg is not far east from the southern
part of this forest; only a little distance from there is Appomattox Courthouse. And west of these ridges, also only
a little way, is where Phil Sheridan rode.

Names of note are connected with these hills and valleys. Woodrow Wilson was born at Staunton, Virginia, on
December 28, 1856. At Lexington between the two southern divisions of the forest are Washington and Lee University, Virginia Military Institute, and the burial places
of Lee and Jackson. Between Lexington and Staunton, just
west of the cross-roads called Midway, where Steele's Tav-
ern has stood, is where Cyrus McCormick invented the
reaper. Farther along state highway 606 is Raphine Hall
and here, it is declared, one Gibbs "invented the sewing
machine" although the shades of Walter Hunt, Elias Howe,
A. B. Wilson, and Isaac M. Singer dispute the claim. We
now leave the Washington National Forest to go on to
take a swift glance at the Monongahela in West Virginia.

The boundaries of the Monongahela encompass some
1,650,000 acres of the roughest of the southern Alleghenys.
This forest was established on April 28, 1920, principally
to stop the burning of timber and ground cover and to
prevent other damage to watersheds that lie at the head
of the Monongahela River. For, in the past, always the
deteriorated watersheds were the big contributors to the
floods at Pittsburgh and other Ohio River communities.

This forest might be called the cradle of mighty rivers.
It embraces 2,300 square miles of watershed. Both the
Potomac and Ohio draw headwater flow from these mountains. Fourteen million people depend on the more than
2,000,000,000 gallons of water per day which these rivers
carry out from this forest. Dead leaves of maple, birch, and
similar hardwood forest trees become water traps as they lie

on the ground. They absorb and hold as much as 150 to 200 times their weight in water. This is only one of the ways a good forest cover helps in preventing floods.

It is expected the yearly timber cut from the Monongahela will be about 25,000,000 board feet per year during the next decade. And this is one eastern forest where there is a limited grazing by domestic livestock: about 2,800 head.

The hill people of the Monongahela country, whose families have lived here since colonial days, have preserved folklore, songs, tales, and even superstitions over the centuries. This is "ramp country." You might never find a printed definition of "ramp" as it is used in the Smoke Hole country of these mountains. Architecturally a ramp is an inclined, stepless structure by which one may get from one level to another. But in the Monongahela it is a very wild onion, eaten as a spring tonic.

In the Monongahela squirrel- and turkey-hunting is engaged in as if it were a ritual. A squirrel call of walnut wood brings the curious bushy-tails out of their hiding. The descendant of a man who toted the first rifled gun barrel into these mountains long, long ago, draws a bead on his game, and there is squirrel stew or pie in the pot that evening.

Turkeys and white-tail deer are hunted in this forest and 1,900 miles of trout streams await the angler. Each year 65,000 sportsmen pay $1 in addition to the state fee to hunt and fish in the Monongahela. The extra dollar is spent on improvement of wildlife habitat. Historically this is elk country, but the last local representative of this great game animal had been shot out by the time Daniel Boone was traveling through here and to Kentucky in the years just before the Revolutionary War.

Near Mill Point within the forest, are curious pieces of

"orphan" land, called the Cranberry Glades. With no similar combination of soil and cover near them, they are "lost" bits of Arctic tundra high in these southern hills.

We have in the Monongahela another experimental forest, the Fernow, which is two and a half miles south of Parsons, West Virginia. Studies are going on here in the second-growth Appalachian hardwood timber stands which can help in management plans of 13,000,000 acres of this type of forest, as the Bartlett experiments in New Hampshire point the way to forest management in northern Appalachian hardwoods.

If you can arrange it, visit Elkins, West Virginia, during its Forest Festival. The sports scheduled during the three days of celebration are of ancient origins. One event traces back to the days of knighthood. In it the riders race their mounts toward a four-inch iron ring that hangs on a string and try to spear the ring with a slim pole—the lance of today's knight of the Smoke Hole country.

The Cumberland National Forest has within its boundary lines approximately 1,333,333 acres. More than 500,000 of these are owned by the federal government. As in the three other southern forests of Region 7, there are improved picnic grounds, camping opportunities, beckoning trails, even a couple of areas where summer homes have been built on plots under special permits.

Local people claim that the biggest dam in eastern United States is located in the Cumberland National Forest, the Wolf Creek Dam. It is 240 feet high, 5,736 feet long, contains 1,380,000 cubic yards of concrete, and 8,900,000 cubic yards of earth fill. The water it impounds turns six generators with a capacity of 62,500 horsepower and 867,000,000 kilowatt hours yearly. The dam holds back 6,089,000 acre-feet of water, which stretch 105 miles upstream, and there is a shoreline that is 1,255 miles long at high water.

The seven national forests in Region 7 contain a gross acreage of about 10,340,000 acres. Of this, approximately 4,250,000 acres are owned by the government. "Purchase units," which are embryonic national forests, number five, and have a gross acreage of 1,012,517. There are two experimental units, Bartlett and Fernow.

Region 7 is where some of our earliest purchased forests were assembled from lands that were badly treated—forests that were ravenously raped as they were logged and became waste lands before their rescue and rehabilitation. All these abused acres were basically forest land that should have been kept busy growing wood and protecting watersheds.

III

'WAY DOWN SOUTH

I

THE southeastern region of our National Forest System, Region 8, includes 11 states. One of these is Texas. Therefore this is the largest region (except Alaska, which is Region 10).

Region 8 presents a variety of topography and many different groupings of plants. Its lands have an array of historical spots linked with events dating back to years before the Revolutionary War.

Several recollections insistently crowd to the fore as I mentally scan Region 8. Although they are not strictly what professionals might regard as within the scope of forestry, they are part of the pulse and breath of this region. As a rule the lives of rural people are entwined with the land and its products. Often we become acquainted more readily with a community through impressions than by studying statistics. Impressions may tell of a land and its people more exactly than tabulations of figures. So such memories of Region 8 as the following are meaningful to me.

Quite a few years ago I was making a study of water pollution, which included the flow in a small river eastward from famed Missionary Ridge near Chattanooga, Tennessee. One rocky, winding side road I traveled each week switched back and forth until I never knew whether we were in Tennessee, northern Georgia, or had strayed into North

Carolina. The route finally ended at a house that was tired, gray, and sagging in the ridgepole.

Down slope from this house, beside the stream where I took the water samples, was the smallest grist mill I ever saw. It had ground no grain for years. The ditch that had carried water to the overshot wheel was full of brambles; a few sizable sycamore saplings also flourished there.

A dour, grayish adult couple lived in the house, which stood on up-ended chunks of tree trunks. Underneath the house was an admirable retreat for dogs, several razorback hogs, and occasionally some of a dozen or so dusty children. A stubble-bearded man who sat on the cluttered porch never offered more than a grudging nod in reply to my greeting. Behind the house was a rocky, rain-gullied field that had grown a hardscrabble cotton crop.

In this field, and in many others near by, on which patient people once had hacked off timber and bush, young, plume-shaped loblolly pines were marching in to reclaim their land. On a chilly day, but one bright with sunshine, I saw two boys gleaning in the rock-flecked cotton patch back of the cabin. The little towhead, who was perhaps four years old, chattered and laughed while his brother, near twenty and totally blind, smiled and felt for the cotton bolls after his hand was guided to the plants by the small lad. The father sat on the cabin porch.

At the time I sensed no parallelism between the small lad and the young pines. In more recent years it has occurred to me that youth, little pines and small boy, represented the future's promise for that part of the south.

Other memories are less austere. There was a day when we got lost in northern Georgia. A wrong turn shunted us into a maze of dirt roads more traveled by mules than by motors. Each wagon trail we took trying to get back to the highway seemed to switch us deeper into a drowsing countryside. It was a gay day and some benign but wayward genius was our unseen guide.

The sun-shot air was suffused with a lambent, golden haze. Where there were holes in leafy canopies of great oaks, sunshine and mist shaped luminous shafts that seemed to hold up the gnarled old treetops. Clots of mistletoe hung in the high branches of ancient trees. Spring whispered to the north Georgia hills.

When the road topped a ridge we saw many smoke columns rising in the valley, banners signaling a stirring around great, time-worn houses that squatted half hidden under the stout oaks. We saw the peach groves through the haze that slightly blurred all objects so they appeared as if in soft focus. Not yet fully in bloom, brushed with new green and pink, these orchards draped like filmy scarves across the knobs that are the last gentle shoulders of the southernmost Appalachians.

There are still more, and different, memory scenes: the cold gray sky of early March, lead-colored puddles of water, a lonesome, abandoned cabin among the blackjack oaks of Arkansas; the grand, laughing, green-robed hills in the Ozarks and the Ouachita mountains, now in national forests bearing these names; the hurry-and-get-there atmosphere of a lumber mill town in east Texas, as pines, such as those in the Crockett and Houston National Forests, went to the saw; the mystery, the enchantment that seemed to enwrap the Great Smokies in a blue which could never be matched by man-made pigment. These are some of my memories of timber country in the south.

II

THERE is a similarity throughout western forest regions
which permits the description of one forest to apply
with slight variations to most units within that region.
This is not so in Region 8. In the 400,000 acres of the
Francis Marion National Forest, with its headquarters at
Columbia, South Carolina, we have conditions and tree
associations approaching the lowland tropics. If we donned
mythical seven-league boots, 4.6 English miles to a league,
we could stride swiftly over to the Sam Houston and Davy
Crockett National Forests in eastern Texas, and find there
pines like those in the Ozarks, but still enough different
for each forest type to have its own character. None of these
would approximate the forests in the southern extension
of the Appalachian mountain system nor duplicate the
man-planted forests in the rolling hills of Mississippi.

Four general classes of forests may be found in Region 8.
The lowland, seaboard, semi-tropical forests represent one
type. The highlands woodlands as found in the Great
Smokies are another. The intermediate upland and roll-
ing-hill forests present a third type, and the Ozarkian
group the fourth. Geological differences have been a principal factor in the evolution of these types.

The highlands of the Appalachian system which extend
into the southeastern region differ from mountain masses
to the north. Over-slips of massive rock plates and long-
axis wrinkling are characteristic of the more northern mountains. In Region 8 a great block of earth crust pushed upward in one otherwise stable chunk. This mixed geological
forms so greatly that even some trained observers might be
baffled by the hodgepodge terrain. The soil types, however,
are not unalike; the climate is much the same on both

sides of the two regions' mutual boundary, where there is a blending of more northern forest types into those found in the south.

Typical monadnocks are features of the landscape in northeastern Region 8. In Maine you may have visited, or at least seen, Mount Monadnock, the individual eminence with the name that applies to all mountains of like origin. A monadnock is a great body of rock that originally squeezed up through a crack in the earth's shell during a period when that rock was plastic as modeling-clay. As this plug of heat-limbered rock thrust up, it elevated overlaying crust above it. Often these coverings were of limestones, sandstones, and shales, the muds of ancient sea bottoms turned to stone.

As the upthrusting core rock cooled, as climates changed, rains, winds, frost, sun's heat, and all the other forces of erosion stripped off the softer overload. The elements leveled the heights until the earth materials spread out in the form of a new plain. But when the claws and gouges of these mountain-wreckers came to the chilled plug of rock that had squeezed out of the planet's molten center, they met adamant resistance.

When you see a rock mountain that looks as if it might have been a plug-like upthrust from far below, a stone peg really—with roots far down in the hot seethings from which volcanoes draw their fire—then you are looking at a monadnock. They are the gravestones of mighty mountains struck down.

The highest mountain east of Harney Peak in the Black Hills National Forest of South Dakota is in Region 8's Great Smokies. It is Mount Mitchell, located a few miles northeast of Asheville, North Carolina, which has an elevation 6,684 feet above sea level.

Asheville is headquarters for three national forests; one

of them is the Pisgah. It stands in relation to American forestry somewhat as Independence Hall does to the nation's beginnings.

When Gifford Pinchot returned from his studies in Europe, there was no rush to bid for his services as a professional forester. There was no embryonic national-forest system that would employ even a dozen men with technical training; no timber companies were hiring men of this profession. In the 1890s any logging-outfit employing a technical forester for his knowledge of timber management would have been hooted out of the woods. No schoolroom learning was needed to drag a saw or swing an ax. It is worthy of passing notice that today there are several times the number of career foresters serving big timber companies in private practice as are found on public payrolls.

Pinchot's chance came when George W. Vanderbilt offered him an opening to manage 7,000 acres of forest on the Biltmore estate out in the hills from Asheville. Pinchot's association with Biltmore began in February 1892. He knew a time would come when men with technical forestry training would be in demand. To prepare for that day, a school, giving all possible basic training in one year of classroom and field work, was organized at Biltmore. Graduates of Biltmore supplied many of Pinchot's executives and disciples when he became head of the newly formed Forest Service in 1905. To the school came young Henry Solon Graves, a Yale graduate, who later succeeded Pinchot as Chief of the Forest Service. From staff work at Biltmore, Graves returned to Yale, there to organize the first graduate course in forestry offered by a major American university.

The opportunity for securing training in forestry was fortified in 1894, when Mr. Vanderbilt purchased some

80,000 acres adjacent to the Biltmore Forest School. Planned management of this woodland, named the Pisgah Forest, was initiated by Gifford Pinchot. When the Weeks Law became effective, the Pisgah and the White Mountain were the first eastern forests to be acquired by the government.

Another tie links all eastern national forests with the Pisgah. Pinchot tells of a group of fellow foresters who gathered around the big fireplace in the Brick House at Biltmore one wintry night in 1892 or 1893. Then Professor Joseph A. Holmes, at the time state geologist of North Carolina, first proposed the purchase of lands to develop national forests in the east. The proposal has become today's reality.

Vanderbilt's selection of the name "Pisgah" may have been deliberate. One reads in the third chapter of Deuteronomy that Moses, denied entrance to the Promised Land, was allowed to climb to the top of the ridge named Pisgah, where Mount Nebo is its highest point, and from there to view "the good land that is beyond Jordan." Like Moses, those early foresters, with Pinchot their leader, did look "westward, and northward, and southward, and eastward" as they hammered away by word and act toward the dream of a promised land which became the national-forest system.

Each forest region has its history, but in none will you find more than in Region 8. Here records of events are layered as leaves of a book, and when you glance at one such page there is another as interesting to follow. The names of the forests call up this land's yesterdays.

One forest is the Cherokee. This is the homeland of a tribesman named George Guess. His Indian name was Sequoyah, and he invented the Cherokee alphabet. It contained 48 letters and therefore was nearer to having a

ymbol of ageless hills is the famed "Old Man of the Mountains," a pro-
in stone, in the White Mountain National Forest in New Hampshire.

Like a breezeway in solid rock, this natural
bridge dominates the skyline of a ridge in the
Cumberland National Forest of Kentucky.

The snow-cloaked Bowl at the head of Tuck
man Ravine in the White Mountain Natio
Forest lures thousands to this popular ha
of ski enthusiasts.

ams hurry down from the Blue Ridge Divide in
ttahoochee National Forest in Georgia. The little
rs tumble and leap from ledges to create lively
shes of beauty. York Creek Falls is one of about
nty such cascades, little known and rarely visited,
are tucked away in the Chattahoochee.

Rhododendrons herald springtime in the southern forests of Region 7.

Fire, usually the terror of the woods, been made to serve good forestry practice Region 8. Controlled flames purge fores diseases and pests and open seed beds to s light.

e startling result of two controlled fires
ows in this picture. A first fire was to clear
ground surface for the seedfall of long-
f pine; the second fire was sent through
s stand of young pines to free them from
brownspot disease.

Sturdy, straight, growing lustily in the Piedmont hills of Georgia, these young loblolly
pines, planted five years before the photo
was taken, are illustrative of the new "farming" of trees as a crop.

This stand of twenty-five-year-old longleaf pine on the Kisatchie National Forest in Louisiana has been thinned to produce a "crop" of fence posts. The remaining trees are relieved of overcrowding, and new wood will be produced here at an accelerated rate.

Straight, stout, and serviceable lumbe[r] being dried, a product of the southern n[ation]al forests where pines are grown and ha[rvest]ed as crops.

untsman continues the Amer-
rifleman's tradition in his na-
l-forest woodland.

ted hillsides collect the waters
ilter them to crystalline clarity
pply the pools where the speck-
rout lurk and the angler casts
eathered flies.

The labyrinthine lakeland of Region 9's Superior National Forest, our greatest northwoods sanctuary of solitude.

In the Superior National Forest of Minne
the level water trails invite you to hund
of miles of primitive travel.

symbol for each vowel and consonant than our alphabet. Another spelling of his name, Sequoia, was given to a great tree to honor a great Indian. It was given also to a national forest and to a national park, both in California.

We did not adopt Sequoyah's alphabet and lost whatever it might have contributed to distinctive American writings. We did take to our heart Uncle Remus and his stories by Joel Chandler Harris, and this is the homeland of both Harris and Remus. Though *we* think of these as delightful folk tales of the Negro, many of the central figures and the stories—the underground panther, the haunted whirlpool, the stone cannibals, and the slant-eyed giant— were first spun beside campfires of the Cherokee Indian.

Unless one has traced the route of De Soto or remembers that he traveled many miles inland, one is likely to think he journeyed only along the Gulf coast. The De Soto National Forest in Mississippi honors this venturing Spaniard.

De Soto did wander far to the north, saw the mountains and surely made camp in the valleys of the Chattahooche National Forest in today's northern Georgia. And you may be surprised to learn that it was De Soto who gave the name of the seacoast-dwelling Apalachee branch of the Muskhogean Indian nation to the whole system of our eastern mountains.

The long, long Appalachian trail has its southern terminus in the Chattahooche forest. Setting out from Mount Oglethorpe, one can travel the ridges of the eastern mountains, a distance of 2,021 miles, to the northern end, that is, to Mount Katahdin in Maine. This is the master trail for all eastern devotees of hiking.

We turn to another page of Region 8's historical background, and everyone recognizes the name Sumter. It now is the name of a national forest in the uplands of South

Carolina. But it also was the famous fort that was fired on at the command of General Beauregard on April 11, 1861, thus opening the Civil War.

Who was Sumter? His given name was Thomas (his intimates called him the Game Cock), he was a native of Virginia, served in the French and Indian War and in the American Revolution. Later he was a Congressman and then a Senator, representing South Carolina.

Francis Marion was the "Swamp Fox" of the American Revolution, the leader of guerillas who struck at British supply lines. Marion fought beside Benjamin Lincoln at Savannah, escaped when Charleston was captured in 1780, and after he led his Colonial commandos on their forays, he showed up in the forces of Light-Horse Harry Lee to trounce the enemy in the decisive battle at Eutaw Springs. The national forest near South Carolina's seacoast is the Francis Marion.

Davy Crockett and Sam Houston are now names of national forests in Texas, and the William B. Bankhead is a forest in Alabama, that statesman's home state. The reasons why these names are honored are obvious. But there is the Apalachicola in northern Florida, which, one may guess, is named for the river that flows there—but how did the river get its name? It commemorates a people that vanished long ago.

The Apalachee Indians built homes and villages and tilled fields. They were peaceful people and often were raided by warlike neighbors. When the British joined their Indian foes, most of the Apalachees were killed, others were captured and sold into slavery, only a remnant escaping to Louisiana. Soon they disappeared. Only the modified name remains: Apalachicola for a Florida town, for a river, for a forest, and Appalachian as the name of the whole mountain system of eastern states.

You will encounter history in every forest of this region. Here, as in all forest regions, color and romance, tragedy and triumph are woven through and around the lands we own.

III

THE outstanding forestry feature of Region 8 is its potential for producing wood.

In the southern forests pines may in 30 to 40 years grow a log large enough to be sawn into lumber rather than tossed into the maws of the pulp machines. This permits profitable "tree-farming." A pure stand of best softwoods is planted; then successive "cropping" of staves, ties, lagging, poles, perhaps spars, follows as thinning prevents overcrowding. The trees finally remaining have had the elbowroom, the nutrients, moisture, and sunlight required to produce select sawlogs.

In the south many pine trees are grown for pulp. When large enough to supply "bolts," they may be clean-harvested, the land cleansed with fire, and a new, pure stand of seedlings planted. Such management puts every acre to growing the most usable wood as opposed to "letting nature take its course" with weed and "wolf" trees in conflict with better types and species.

In contrast, about 60 to 70 years are needed for pines of the Lake states and New England to reach sawlog size. There also a spruce will loaf along through 100 years before it is thick enough in its stem to take to the lumber mills; hardwood trees in these states require average growing-periods of 120 years for producing sawlogs.

On the Pacific coast Douglas firs and hemlocks reach full maturity in about 100 years. Even so, if, after pausing where you can see the stands of mature Douglas fir—the really "virgin" blocks that remain in the Northwest—you will look at the shaggy trunks, 30 or 40 inches in diameter, and then at the young forest boiling up from adjacent cleared areas, you will marvel that any of these small trees could be as big a century hence as the old uncut firs are.

The south's potential for producing more wood of high quality lies, of course, in the almost continuous growing-season and the abundant precipitation. Alabama's growing-season is 200 to 250 days; even 300 days in her southwest corner. With this there is an average rainfall of 54 inches.

Perhaps I can emphasize how pregnant the south is, as our most bountiful wood-producing region, by contrasting how slowly trees grow in my own adopted country of the Rocky Mountain west. Among our most rapid growers is the lodgepole pine, a semi-weed that rushes in to staple down the soil after fire sweeps away spruce or pines. Under the best conditions the lodgepole pine will grow large enough in some 80 years to "cut out" ties or be peeled, its butt creosoted to protect it against rot, and put in service as a utility pole. But this 80-year period for lodgepole to grow to a size large enough for poles or railroad ties is a minimum from seed to felling. In the south pines grow that big in 20 to 30 years.

Colorado can serve as the average and representative state. The precipitation ranges from a desert-dry 7 inches per annum in the San Luis valley, which lies in the south-central portion of the state, to nearly 30 inches in high mountain valleys, which are efficient cloud traps. The frost-free days number 189 at Grand Junction in southwestern Colorado's "peach belt," 141 at Arriba on the plains about 100 miles east of Denver, and only 60 at Steamboat

Springs, a mountain community in the north-central part
of the state.

Recently a friend who collects oddities of nature's handi-
craft gave me a cross-section of the western red cedar, often
called "Jay Scop," a shortened version of *Juniperus scopu-
lorum*. Jay Scop is a relative of the Virginia red cedar,
which is listed *J. virginiana* in the botany books. Neither
are true cedars, and both are only moderate in size at
maturity, but they are strikingly attractive evergreens,
whether standing in columnar dignity on our lawns or sawed
into fragrant bits of claret-colored lumber to line chests and
moth-proofed closets.

With care, such as received in home gardens, Jay Scop
grows with fair velocity; there are a number in Denver
gardens which I watched being planted when I was in
professional landscape practice. These have stretched from
3 feet as youngsters to nearly 30 feet. But the tree from
which the cross-section had been sliced must have grown
in a dry location, and perhaps at the upper limit in altitude
at which Jay Scop can survive. When I put this slice of tree
trunk under a magnifying glass and counted the rings, I
found that the tree had lived for not less than 120 years.
It was only three inches in diameter; the 120 rings were
all packed in the 1½ inches from the center to the
outer rim.

This is a rather extreme case to cite, but it does suggest
the importance of assigning all our southern forest land
—where trees grow so rapidly—to wood production.

While I will agree with the poet that "only God can
make a tree," I must add that in the forests of the southeast ordinary men are beginning materially to help the
Good Lord and husband the trees He makes. While the
tree-farm idea may have begun in the Pacific northwest, it

has taken root, literally as well as figuratively, in the southeast. The position of the national forests in Region 8 is that of the vanguard in a new era in American forestry.

Most of the southern forest country is owned by corporations and individuals. Large timber and pulp companies have applied tree-farm management to lands they already owned and to lands they have bought with the long-range objective of growing wood on them. When they caught up this "new" idea, the companies had years of experimentation and field methods developed in the national forests of Region 8 to guide them. This has been an important service in basic forestry performed in this region by the national forests.

I V

THE national forests of Region 8 contain a gross area of nearly 19,000,000 acres. Title to only about half of this acreage is vested in the government.

The Weeks Law carries no power of eminent domain. Should a government offer to purchase be refused by an owner, there may be appraisals and then an agreement on price, but under this law the government cannot acquire privately owned woodland without consent of the owner. Thus there still are a number of the eastern forests with blocks of land that are being bargained for—as owner and government try to arrive at a price acceptable to both parties. Other private properties are not being considered for purchase; they are more valuable as small farms. Income from small, forest-encircled farms may not be enough to maintain a home, but seasonal employment may be available in the woods, and a combination of farming and timber jobs often will support a family.

Nineteen million acres are within the exterior boundaries of the 26 forests in Region 8, but only half of these are federal property. A dozen "purchase units" where some lands have been acquired have a gross area of 1,000,000 acres; of these 170,000 are government owned. Some day, if conditions merit, these may expand into full-fledged national forests. The Forest Service in this region also manages more than 500,000 acres of what are known as "LU lands."

Region 1, which is mostly in Montana, administers more than 3,000,000 acres having this "LU" status, and Region 2 has nearly 2,250,000 such acres to care for in Wyoming and Colorado. Nationally the LU lands exceed 7,000,000 acres. LU is an easier way of saying Land Utilization. These lands came into the care of the U.S. Forest Service by way of the Soil Conservation Service, partly because the U.S.F.S. has among the bureaus the most experience in proper management of livestock grazing on federal lands.

When the depression and the mid-1930s drought began to pound to bits the hopes and fortunes of people who had been trying to farm semi-arid and marginal crop land, they turned to Washington for rescue. The buying-program which followed included pastures and livestock ranges that had been generally overloaded until the raw earth was exposed and bled away under wind and rain. The grain fields purchased were sick and overworked; they never had been suited to tillage and should have remained in grass or forest.

When it became public estate, the tired earth was allowed to rest. It was given a cloak of new grasses to heal the sores where winds and cloudbursts had ripped away its humus blanket. Increased rain in the seasons that followed helped the grasses grow and aided healing of the soil's surface. The land became fruitful again, and a limited number of livestock was allowed to graze on it. The land even gained in productive capacity. Other uses that would not jeopardize the soil wealth of these purchased areas were also allowed.

By 1957 sound conservation principles had achieved such good results on most of these lands that some people desired possession of them. Transferring the LU lands to the U.S. Forest Service administration was a first maneuver in a devious scheme to "sell them back to their owners." A strange situation showed up when politicians and certain cattlemen began to insist that this be done. Other livestock operators who held leases on the rehabilitated acres opposed the sale of the LU lands to the *alleged* "former owners." Most of the "former owners" had never owned or even leased a foot of these lands; they just wanted to acquire the properties at a bargain price. They failed in that scheming.

The LU lands are comparable to abused orphans placed in public custody to protect them. The Soil Conservation Service was the first public custodian, and it applied the regimen of conservation which returned them to good health. Now under the management of the Forest Service they may have found a home among the land-use types administered by this agency. Remember, therefore, that while these lands are within the U.S.F.S. at the present time, they did not arrive there as lands purchased because they were primarily best suited to forest management, but were transferred because of their condition, which can best be described by the term "beat up." The Forest Service acts as their guardian.

V

IN ITS strictly forest units the southeastern region presents a long list of both plant and animal residents. Let us glance briefly at this region's wealth of flora and fauna.

At tidewater are two species of cypress, the pond and the bald. They will be found displaying their pitcher-butted trunks and "knees" in the coastal-plain forests—the Crotan in North Carolina, the Oceola, the Ocala, the Apalachicola of Florida, the De Soto of Mississippi. The pines, grouped as "yellow pines" or as the "2- and 3-needle pines," live in the intermediate zone between lowland and mountain heights. This intermediate belt we call the "piedmont," a name borrowed from the tenth-century kingdom of the Lombards in Italy. Now used generically, the term characterizes any alluvial bench-land—a foothill plateau of high fertility—but it often is used specifically to designate certain defined areas in the Carolinas and northern Georgia.

The "yellow" pines of the piedmont in Region 8 are the longleaf, the Cuban (which is of little importance), the loblolly (which with the longleaf makes the important team of softwood lumber and pulp trees of the region), and the pitch pine, shortleaf pine, Virginia pine, and spruce pine.

The eastern or Virginia red "cedar," though of no such commercial importance as its coniferous cousins, the longleaf and loblolly pines, supplies the most emphatic accents of any tree in the region's landscapes. Often growing as single specimens, this evergreen lends rhythm and accent to the woodlands. Or regimented along ridges, seen against the smoky reds and yellows of a southern sunset, the cedar becomes the hallmark of the south's mountain forests.

The deciduous hardwoods blend and merge with the evergreens on either margin and throughout the piedmont, but they come into their own land on the hilly uplands. The flowering dogwood, sugar, red, and silver maples; box-elder; blue, white, and pumpkin ash; Ohio buckeye; black walnut; butternuts; five different hickories; honey locust; and black locust are native in Region 8. Here is the stronghold of the sassafras tree. Also we find the red mulberry, Osage orange, sweet gum, sycamore, yellow poplar, magnolia, sweet bay, cucumber tree, tupelo, persimmon, American and slippery elms, white basswood, hackberry, willows, cottonwoods, beeches, chestnuts, and oaks. Certainly there have been tree species of some importance that I've left out. For instance I might list 20 different species of oaks found somewhere in Region 8.

There is a special time to see the woods of Region 8—particularly those of the Appalachian uplands—and that is when the flowering shrubs break out their bouquets. The redbud or Judas tree pops open its pea-like blossoms in the first third of April. In the Ozark and Ouachita country of Arkansas and Oklahoma I have seen the redbud and wild-plum blooms explode simultaneously; count it a lucky season if you can find this bit of wild splendor on the hillsides.

From mid-April to early in May the flowering dogwood fills the forest's understory with its drifts of snow-white bloom. Through late June to early July the mountain laurel, the pink rhododendron, and the flame azalea are on show—and after the full pageantry of summer is past, there is the blaze and fire of foliage lit by the first tickle of the high country's frosty weather.

I should interpolate that here, as in every part of the nation, you must remember that flowering time is geared to the season, the general climate pattern, and the current

weather. There is a rough rule that for every 1,000 feet
gained in elevation as one travels up mountain slopes, there
is an average decrease in temperature of 3½ degrees. At the
top of some of Region 8's mountains which are almost a
mile above sea level, the temperatures average nearly 20 degrees lower than in the forests along the seacoast. This does
not hold as an absolute formula; it applies far more in the
west, where we have mountains that are nearly three miles
above sea level. The point to remember, however, is that,
though spring and summer march northward across the
level lands, they march *up* the mountain sides. The ground
phlox that grows like moss on granite ledges in the Rocky
Mountains often blooms in the foothills late in April, but
one can see it blooming at 11,000 feet altitude, near timberline, in August.

V I

The southland's quail-hunting, turkey-shooting, possum
and coon hunts, the variety of waterfowl-shooting in
coastal areas, squirrel-hunting—these sports have been her-
alded and bragged about. Less widely publicized are the
game species found in the southern woodlands. Region 8's
wildlife includes white-tail deer, black bears in the southern Appalachians, Florida, and the Ozarks, and trans-
planted European wild boar. Some grouse inhabit this region and dove-shooting, not in the woods but in the openings and in near-by fields, is popular. Each year 200,000
hunters become the harvesters of any game surpluses, and
through their license fees supply the funds to maintain
wildlife management in their states.

A third of a million trout fishermen angle in the

streams of Region 8's national forests. The native trout are
called "speckled trout" in the south, brook trout in other
sections of North America. If you should happen to get
into a beaver pond which is jumping with little brookies so
small they are not legal size, little fish that hit big artificial
flies with impudence and abandon, you will have your own
names for the family of *Salvelinus fontinalis*, the char we
cherish as our native eastern brook trout.

Along with the brookies are two fairly close relatives,
the rainbow and the brown trout. They are "foreigners."
The rainbow is a native of our streams that drain into the
Pacific Ocean—and mostly north of mid-California. The
brown-trout stock, a thorough mix and blend through artificial propagation of Loch Leven and "German" brown
trout, came from streams and lakes of the British Isles and
countries across the Channel and the North Sea. Rainbows
and browns will persist in streams that are too warm for
other trout; the brown trout will tough his way through
waters carrying more suspended silt.

Hunters and fishermen are only a part of the 10,000,000
visitors who come to the national forests in Region 8. Some
visitors are sightseers traveling through; others stop for a
little while. More than 160 areas have been equipped for
picnicking, camping, and viewing the scenery from high
overlooks. Eighty improved camping-areas invite overnight
occupancy. Some campgrounds are developed to accommo-
date trailer homes. Camps operated by organizations—Boy
Scouts, Girl Scouts, Campfire Girls, church groups, and
others—are active for 24 or more weeks each year. Sites on
which private summer homes may be located are permitted, with a modest annual fee charged for this use.

I realize that there is more interest for most visitors in
the flash of white you see as the buck deer plunges away in

the thickets of a ferny glen, or in the folklore of the mountains, than in the important fact that Region 8 grows pines nearly twice as fast as any other section of the nation. Nevertheless this is a fact of importance to you. The adequacies of future supplies of wood pulp for newspapers, shopping-bags, soft tissues, and all the other necessities that come from wood cellulose are linked to the swift-growing trees in Region 8.

Unless fire or another scourge has completely cleared lands of seed trees, nature often will re-establish forests on areas that should be growing forests. These seed trees may be seed-bearing culls left as logging has taken the straight and solid ones. Or seed may be brought in by wind or bird from some distance, and thus replant the bared acres. The prevention of fires, above every other measure, permits these natural forces to rebuild a forest laid low by logging or flames. It is true that the weed trees may rush in to claim the land so completely that the better types cannot find space to live in, but it is as true that these less-desirable trees, often quick of growth and soft of fiber, nail the soil in place, build humus back into the soil surface, and conserve moisture, thus becoming a nurse crop for the young of better tree varieties. In many cases this natural cycle requires such a long time to arrive at a full stocking of preferred lumber species that we have to plant the kinds of trees which give best returns.

The re-establishment of young forests on lands that have been cleared of sawlog timber is most often accomplished merely by protection against fire. Even on very large areas called "tree farms"—and "farm" suggest planting and harvesting—there may be no setting out of young trees. In some places, however, small trees must be planted. If they are spaced 5 by 5 feet the count will be 1,742 seedlings per acre—a plot approximately 210 by 210 feet.

We have about 50,000,000 acres of unproductive forest land which must be planted by man either with seeds or small trees if those acres are again to grow timber. Planting must be on a mass basis even to set up a hope that the job can ever be done.

A mechanical tree-planter is an oddly shaped machine. In action one man drives the tractor pulling it, while a second man sits on the planter, bent forward above a double-faced plow that cuts a furrow. At regular intervals the second man feeds a seedling tree into the mechanism. The machine places the seedling's roots in the furrow and two wheels, one on either side and at the angle, press soil around the roots. By such mechanical aids millions of little trees have been planted throughout the south. Acres are planted where no natural regeneration of forest cover could occur also. A very new practice is to plant one species on treeless land, secure a pure stand, and expect to "crop" this "field" as one would any farm land.

In the midlands, the piedmont belt, between the semi-tropical coastal forests and the hardwood highlands, are the field plantings of pines. In every respect, these properties are being *farmed*, and the crop is wood. One such unit representative of the whole program is the Chickasawhay division of the De Soto National Forest in southeastern Mississippi.

VII

The boundaries of the De Soto National Forest surround 1,213,740 acres; of these, 500,444 are publicly owned. The Chickasawhay unit of the De Soto was set up as a purchase area in 1934. By 1936 the unit contained 130,900 acres of federal land in a total of 204,800 acres.

Many different forces had been at work on this land. There had been clearings for farms that failed, burnings for many reasons, war, depression, one-cropping. Less than 10 per cent of the total was adequately stocked with timber. Only 689 acres were stocked with more than 25 per cent of desirable pine species—not much of a start from which to go on to a forest with the straight-lined, regimented trees, all of a size, managed for recurrent croppings.

On this Chickasawhay unit the job was one of fully regenerating a timber stand on land from which it had been almost completely wiped away by abuse.

There was a dearth of readily serviceable roads on this unit. Those that did exist were of low grade and became quagmires in wet spells; they were beds of powdery dust during droughts. Trying to get to a fire or to a planting-area was a frustrating job. For tree-planting and normal administration there had to be roads; for fire prevention and suppression there had to be lots of *good*, all-season roads.

By 1956, 294 miles of roads had been built in the Chickasawhay unit. Fire-fighters could get swiftly to where a blaze had started. The next step was to install a fire-alarm system. Six steel fire towers with lookout crow's-nests at their tops were erected on this part of the De Soto.

The first plantings were by hand methods. In four years 28,870 acres were planted with seedlings. These little trees made a surprising record—only 25 acres had to be replanted. By 1941, 122,327 acres of the Chickasawhay unit had been planted; then the war halted this work. During the war only 3,355 more acres were planted. Recently machines have taken over the job of planting the baby trees.

Wildfire was the number 1 enemy of the young forests on the De Soto. This is also "razorback country"—they were the young pines' number 2 enemy. These hogs are not the imported wild boars classed as game animals, but big-boned, bacon-sided, genuine, high-slung piney-woods root-ers. And they rooted. They played havoc, digging with their snouts to get at the tender pine roots and other deli-cacies.

Traditionally cows were allowed to run at large through the timberlands. Lean and hungry, they may not have chosen bud tips of young pines as first-preference forage, but they developed an appetite that destroyed hundreds of loblolly and longleaf pine seedlings. They trampled the forest floor and broke young trees as they stepped on them. The third necessity on the Chickasawhay unit was a hog-tight and cow-high fence around the timberlands.

This young, southern tree farm started almost from scratch in 1934. By the time we entered World War II it was possible to thin some of the woodlands, and this unit supplied a yearly average of 200,000 board feet in pulp bolts processed by distillation for turpentine, resins, pine tar and related products. Thinning and additional uses de-veloped as the trees became larger.

The annual *increment* of wood on the Chickasawhay unit was estimated at 12,000,000 board feet on approxi-mately 131,000 acres. The first harvest of trees grown from the first-planted seedlings was in 1951. Seventeen years had elapsed from the planting to the first harvest by thinning. 122,165 board feet of pine lumber were cropped, as were 27,450 board feet of hardwood lumber, taken to further convert the land to the pure-stand pine crop, and 315,000 board feet that went as pulp. All of this further improved the timber stand.

This is the story of growing wood on only a part of one of the 26 forests in the southeastern region.

.   .   .

One management practice current on southland forests appears to be against all forestry dicta. In the southern forests, fire is used as a tool of management.

Southern settlers in the very early days began burning the lowland country to get rid of rank dead grass and litter. After a flash fire ran through the scattered timber, the grass would come green and fresh. As the people moved on to the piedmont and mountain country they took this "light-burning" idea with them. If it was good in one place, they decided, it would be good in another. But the initial value in this practice was lost sight of. Any burning became regarded as good; that was not so in many cases. Hurtful fire was the major agency that cleaned timber off many southern forests past recovery.

Foresters who came to the piney woods country from other regions had had the idea that all fire in timberlands was bad. But they saw a few signs indicating that perhaps in these pine areas it could also serve. Fire cleanses. A fungus disease called "brown spot" is a killer of the south's young pines; it defoliates them, destroying the needles. With a fast-running, light-burning fire sweeping just above the ground, the land and the young trees are cleansed, just as flaming a platinum needle in a bacteriology laboratory kills all the germs on it. The lower pine needles, those infected, are destroyed in flame, but usually if the terminal bud is not killed, the tree will live, and once it has reached sapling size it cannot be struck down by the disease.

Fire also has been used in this region to rid the land of less desirable plant growth that can choke out the valuable young pines. And fire has another use in the south. Loblolly pines will not reseed in an area that is lush with grasses and bushes; they like the bare soil as a nursery site, and if fire can give those conditions, the pine comes in fast and abundant.

Controlled, directed, and held from spilling into destructive size, fire has been accepted as a "tool" in southern forest-management plans.

VIII

THIS southland is the heath of the little Oceola deer, a race of the white-tail species. It is also magnolia land; it is the land of hominy grits, rice, corn pone, possum and coon hunts, and the utterly indefinable blue of the Great Smokies after a spring rain.

You will visit the southland if you ever hope to store away the pleasure of hours and days, sunshine and rain, which you'll encounter in Region 8. But above all, here is the place where, both in demonstration programs and in their full expansion, we must look to our best wood-producing acres being assigned to the high service of growing timber.

The south holds the opportunity for the full fruition of the tree-farming idea. Here one may find affirmation of common ideas as to what forestry is, or should be—rows of trees planted, mile after mile, straight as soldiers at attention.

On the heights of the Pisgah or Cherokee or the Nantahala National Forests in the southernmost Appalachians you can see the tumble of the old mountains with their coves and balds; in the Ocala or the Oceola or the Apalachicola National Forests in Florida you can see the Spanish moss, cypress, even an alligator in some still pool. For Region 8 is a realm of forest variety.

IV

BUNYAN, THE BARON, AND BRULÉ

I

SURELY the prodigious deeds of Paul Bunyan are as well known as the adventures of Br'er Rabbit, the Tar Baby, and their neighbors in the southland. Paul strode in mythical majesty across the northern states now in the Forest Service's Region 9.

This giant woodsman felled mile-square tracts of trees with one swipe of his ax. He completely logged off the Dakotas so those states could be settled by homesteading farmers. Babe, Bunyan's Great Blue Ox, tramped around northern Minnesota, leaving hoofprints that filled with water—and that is how Minnesota got her 10,000 lakes.

I have great respect for Paul's prowess. In 1919, 1921, and again in later years I saw lingering evidence of the havoc he visited on forests of our lake states. Only a mighty man could have wrought so much destruction as he produced square miles of lumber.

We think of Paul as a folk hero of burly stature, a bearded, rock-rough giant endowed with a heart of gold. We don't think of him as being woods boss for another, somewhat more real figure, the Timber Baron. The Baron is the well-preserved target of those who spend more time assailing non-conservation acts of yesterday's lumbermen than they give to supporting current rehabilitation programs in our forests.

Paul is actually a two-faced legend. He was a great wil-

[99]

derness-tamer, but his methods were wasteful. He represents the spirit of a brand of enterprise which was responsible for the reckless logging of the lake states' forests. More than free enterprise, it was at times wanton exploitation. I do not gloss over what the worst of the historic spoilers of the northern pineries did to those woodlands. Certainly they willfully highgraded these forests but that was the mode of lumbering in the period. If any timber operator had not faced current economic facts and met his competition, he would have gone broke.

Inconsistently we hardly murmur against the more complete destruction of forests that grew on the black-soil farm land of present-day Ohio, Indiana, Illinois, Iowa, and Missouri. Most of this good land found in the "belly of the country" is dark and rich, because throughout many, many centuries, after the ice sheets shrank back toward the north, these acres sustained a wonderful forest. These lost woodlands also were spread over lands now within Region 9.

The stout hardwood trees of these states gave their mite to aid settlement. After the pioneers notched logs to form walls of their homes and barns, halved other logs to make floor puncheons, split poles to make rails for fences, and whittled a few sticks into furniture and utensils, nearly all other trees were cut, stacked, and given to the torch. Beyond these meager, though important uses of wood for housing and home, those forests of the central states were junked.

In contrast, though the men of Paul Bunyan's breed ripped and tore through the northern forests, they did send out lumber to build homes and towns across the high-rolling prairies. Man-set fires in the lake states did change acres of brushy slash to ashes. But in the north woods there was far less deliberate destruction of sound logs

merely to get rid of them than there was in the embryonic
farm belt of the Midwest. And after they departed, Paul
Bunyan and the Timber Baron left the land to nature's
healings. The farmer fought off the forest wherever it tried
to re-establish itself. It is well he did; those acres were
destined to grow food.

What happened to the major forests of our midlands was
mostly dictated by necessity. Farmer and logger both were
realists. Their first consideration was to stay alive, economically and physically. If there was waste or ruthlessness,
they accepted these as incidental to sustaining life.

You may regard me as rather tolerant toward the Timber Baron and his Paul Bunyan woodsmen. I have re-
marked that I had observed, as early as 1919, the aftermath
of their invasion of the lake states pineries. Strictly as a
feeling stemming from emotion I could throw my most
scorching invective at them, and I would do so with far
more background and feeling than most of those who flay
yesterday's timber operators, considering it smart and
somehow patriotic to damn their acts. Perhaps this is no
valid reason for my having what seems tolerance toward
the northwoods timbermen, but it was some Paul working
for a Baron who logged the white pine that Valentine
Smith nailed into one stout, Midwest-type frame house
which faces on Sioux Avenue in Mapleton, Iowa. I was
born in that house. It was a good shelter, and it housed a
home. Although it was built in the 1880s, it still serves
well as a family domicile.

There was a bond between the trees and the builders
who fashioned the "cork pine" from the lake country into
houses, churches, schools, towns, and kitchen cupboards
and bread boards. As these master craftsmen sawed the
pine, the severed wood gave off a sweet odor. The other

carpenter in our town beside Val Smith was Mister Brown. I never heard him called anything else, and the "Mister" was a mark of respect.

Mister Brown had a shop where he shaped with hand tools the town's cabinets, cupboards, shelving, and whatnots. Today these oddments are either made of scentless steel or are obtainable ready-made in standardized plywood units. Mister Brown was white-haired, a member of the G.A.R., often incapacitated by aches. His gnarled fingers were deft, and when he shoved his plane the length of a clear, white pine board, the shaving curled away in a continuous ribbon. Then the smell of the wood fortified the incense of industry that always hung in that sawdusty shed behind the Brown residence.

Between 1870 and 1900 the secondary railway lines were spreading out over the treeless stretches west of the Mississippi as rapidly as pumpkin vines run under July sunshine. At more or less regular intervals of eight to a dozen miles, a town was platted beside the rails. Some "died in the shell" as my dad would have put it. Others hatched into the wooden-house villages and towns, which sometimes grew into the steel and concrete cities of modern mid-America.

The logging in the lake states during the latter half of the nineteenth century was profligate and wasteful, sometimes blackened with records of brazen boodling. But lumber from those areas did build the towns of our middle border. I wonder what other material could have been made available at so reasonable cost to build those communities.

The older and larger national forests in Region 9 are in northern Michigan, Wisconsin, and Minnesota. The region is bounded on the north by that almost invisible international boundary between the United States and

Canada. Ohio, Michigan, Indiana, Illinois, Missouri, Iowa, and North Dakota are the other states in this region.

There are as yet no national forests in Iowa or North Dakota. There are, however, three purchase units in Iowa. The gross area of the Chariton, Chequest, and Keosauqua units is 218,671 acres, but by 1957 only about 5,000 acres within exterior boundaries had been purchased by the federal government. These may never grow enough to be designated national forests. In North Dakota there are two purchase units, three LU units; and the Forest Service administers more than 1,000,000 acres of federal lands in this state with practically all of it the treeless LU grazing-lands.

As we head northward out of the southeastern region toward our goal the Superior National Forest in northern Minnesota, we pass near forests located in Missouri and the three states directly north of the Ohio River. Missouri has two national forests: the 1,972,304-acre Clark and the 1,349,537-acre Mark Twain. Both are in the Ozark country. Within the gross areas are 1,351,888 acres owned by the government.

Ohio has one national forest, the Wayne, with a gross area of 1,454,982 acres, about 105,000 of these owned by the government. Indiana has one forest, and one LU unit, the total acreage approaching 750,000, the government-owned land being about 120,000 acres. The Shawnee National Forest is tucked far down in the southern toe of Illinois.

Often places of charm and beauty and paths or places of historical significance lies just off the main thorough-fares. The Shawnee National Forest is such a passed-by area. It is in the Illinois Ozarks; its highest point—the second highest spot in the state—Williams Hill near the town of Herod, is topped by a fire-lookout tower. This tower gives a high overlook across miles of landscape. The western section of the Shawnee contains the wooded bluffs along the east side of the Mississippi northward from Cairo. The forest contains 801,944 acres, of which 203,000 are federal lands.

The pamphlet furnished by the Forest Service contains directions for the way to Pounds Hollow, where there is a picnic site, a 34-acre lake for fishing, and an old Indian campsite. Also, near Jonesboro, at the site of the old Union County Fairgrounds, is the monument marking the spot where in 1859 Lincoln and Douglas held their third debate. The ruins of an old Illinois furnace, where ore was smelted before the Civil War, is 6 miles north of Rosiclare, the local "Old Stone Face" is 8½ miles southeast of Harrisburg, and the Pomona Natural Bridge, of limestone and 85 feet long, is 9½ miles south of Murphysboro. The Kaskaskia Experimental Forest is part of this forest.

The Shawnee offers the chance to become acquainted with the typical hardwood forests of mid-America. It also is at the northern limits of the shortleaf pine's natural range.

The Missouri Ozarks are a realm of their own—neither is this hill country the same as the Blue Ridge and other mountains to the east, nor is this stream-cut plateau akin to the highlands to the west.

It has been quite a few years since my wife and I followed the highway north from Texarkana, the city with the Texas-Arkansas state boundary bisecting it. The highway—through the area now within the Quachita and Ozark forests—led toward Springfield, Missouri. I hope the highway north from Harrison, Arkansas, has not been materially changed, for it was one of those roads in no great hurry to get anywhere. It swung its lazy curves around the hills' shoulders—or it dipped into a valley here, a glen at another spot, and invited one to linger. Climbing to high ridges somewhere near the Arkansas-Missouri line, for some miles it snaked a nearly level course around the higher knobs, deftly ducking across the saddles between little peaks.

On this stretch of road, at a place where we had a far overlook into valleys clothed with oaks and their associates, we once halted beside a roadside stand. It displayed baskets for sale. They were not common baskets, though they could be called homely. They resembled in their way the spare man in the dark trousers and shirt who made and sold them; there was a quality in the man which suggested the straight-grained, tough, unsmoothed but stout split hickory wythes out of which the baskets were woven. It is a comment on wood and worker that after a quarter century in which it was booted around and roughly handled, the basket we bought still remained a good container for our smaller garden tools.

The forests of more southern parts of Region 9 are predominantly of hardwood trees. They contain the last fragments of those oak, hickory, elm, basswood, sycamore, yellow poplar, and related type forest stands which were so thoroughly cleared away and mainly burned to make way for the good farms. Perhaps a few hidden pockets where the ax and flame did not erase all the virgin hardwoods still exist. More significant are the resurgent native trees in the national forests. Those original forests were lost so completely that the passenger pigeons no longer could find adequate, suitable nesting places. Biologists now believe the loss of forest habitat was as much to blame for the extinction of these birds as was hunting for markets.

We have rescued some few species from the passenger pigeons' fate. The whooping cranes' battle to survive has been a desperate one. Bison came close to disappearing before they were rescued. We accept Buffalo Creek as a Wyoming place name without question; we think of the western plains and foothills as the bisons' homeland. But there is another Buffalo Creek that empties into the eastern tip of Lake Erie; a New York village derived its name from that creek and grew into a city. There are three Elktons in eastern states; in Todd County, Kentucky, in Cecil County, Maryland, and a third in the northern portion of Virginia's Shenandoah Valley. Long ago there were wapiti in these eastern states. And there were bison in northern New York.

The last flock of prairie chickens I remember seeing in Iowa flew into our corn field one dullish autumn day when, as a youngster, I prowled the banks of Newman Creek, which cut through our farm, with my black-and-white shepherd dog named Bouncer. Air throbbed as wings beat to slow the impact of landing, and I ran to tell my father, who hurried toward the field carrying the old double-barrel shotgun—although it was illegal even then to shoot those birds. The fried prairie chicken tasted no less appetizing because of unenforced game laws.

It took many years for wildlife officials to learn that it was not the impact of hunting which played a primary part in beating down species originally as abundant as were the pigeons, bison, elk, and prairie chickens as much as it was the environmental changes man imposed on these wild residents of plains and forests. Years after that one taste I ever had of fried prairie chicken, I tramped Colorado's eastern plains with Stokley Ligon, one of the modern west's great naturalists. A little flock of prairie chickens winged from autumn-browned wild grass ahead of us. The plow more than shotguns, said Ligon, sent the prairie chickens sliding downward. The hen of this species is more demanding than the most opinionated housewife;

there must be little thickets of last year's bluestem grass to nest in, or this female grouse will not do her stint in providing the eggs and brooding that bring forth new chicks.

Long ago some who held regard for history began to battle for the preservation of material things associated with the beginnings of the nation. We preserve the Declaration of Independence, the Constitution, Independence Hall, even Fort Laramie, the Cabrillo Lighthouse, and the Alamo. But we have been so busy "subduing the wilderness," we have almost subdued it out of existence. True wild country with all its natural denizens, mobile or stationary, is as much a part of the American heritage as any structure, place, document, or chattel. We are desperately close to having insufficient wild lands remaining.

Perhaps there is no need to concern ourselves greatly with the loss of wilderness. It may be that physicians and psychiatrists will find antidotes administered subcutaneously in office or sanitarium to dispel the tensions causing heart failures and mental upsets. But until they find a pill or potion, or a serum by syringe, which can completely substitute for the peace that the wilderness gives bountifully, we must have wildlands of size. For in wilderness there is a gift of peace more real for many than what is found in any man-fashioned edifice.

There is no higher service that the forests can supply to individual and community than the healing of mind and spirit which comes from the hours spent where there is great solitude. It is significant that people who have experienced the fullness of wilderness living, specifically men of the forests, have initiated and labored for keeping some parts of them as wildland sanctuaries.

Some 80 areas within the national forests have been designated as roadless, wild, or as wilderness sanctuaries.

Though the struggle to preserve the heart of Region 9's Superior National Forest as the last roadless fastness of wilderness canoe travel has not entirely ended, this forest actually was the site of the first battles to save a bit of real national-forest wild country. With rather full knowledge of all the labors of the many who fought, desperately at times, to preserve the now-famous Quetico-Superior country, it is my belief that there has been more shaping and tempering and annealing of the "wilderness idea" in connection with the preservation of the Superior forest roadless area than with any other public property. I make this statement with full cognizance of the wilderness portions of the national parks and their protection and preservation under park laws.

Several factors differentiate the wilderness areas set aside in the national forests and those in the national parks. The laws that established the parks set up barriers against material exploitation. The forests' reason for being, first of all, was to provide materials for use. Then to set aside a block of land within a forest where there would be no intrusion of structures or internal combustion engines of any kind, no priority of logging or grazing of domestic stock, involved a complete reshaping of outlook on the part of a good many people. The story of the establishment of the Superior roadless area is a case history of the recognition and establishment of wilderness as a proper land use in national forests.

II

The Superior National Forest lies in the northernmost part of Minnesota, in the "Arrowhead Country." Look at the map and you will find the tip of the arrow point where the boundary between Canada and the United States crosses the shoreline of Lake Superior. The south side of the "arrow" is the lake shore northeast of Duluth. The northern side is the International Boundary as it follows a northwesterly course from Lake Superior up the Pigeon River and over the "height of land" between this stream and the creeks that flow toward Lake Winnipeg.

Once there was a great mountain range rising above the land where the Superior forest now lies. That was before the ice came. What the highlands were like before the glaciers began to flow up, over, and down the sides of the Mesabi mountains is of little concern to us at this moment. There are not enough of the Mesabi's peaks left greatly to affect the face of this country; the remaining stubs of those high peaks that were cut down are mere mounds.

The smash-up of both rock and ice which occurred here as the glaciers spread down from the north must have been almost beyond human comprehension. As if they were guardians of the great savannas of what then was central North America, the mountains held back the ice for a long time. The ice finally topped the ridges in a great upthrusting slide and dived down the southern sides to scoop deep and dig the basin of our biggest fresh-water ocean—Lake Superior. At its maximum depth, the bottom of the lake is 690 feet below sea level. Its surface is 602 feet above sea level, its greatest length is 420 miles, and its greatest width 167 miles. This hole suggests the power and the weight of the sheets of ice which tore down the mountains of Mesabi.

Sometimes the ice shrank; sometimes it gathered new velocity moving feet per hour where it had stood still or moved inches per day. Once it had topped the Mesabi it twisted and squeezed and crushed, like a python, reducing its hard-ribbed prey, the mountains, to a formless pulp.

Much of the smashed-up mountains was carried far to the south. Not once, but time after time, the ice shoved rock, rubble, and splintered forests far down the great central basin. As the ice pushed it also scoured away all the plant life.

Chaos came to the Mesabi range. Pinnacles were knocked down, granite foundations planed off. Some valleys were gouged deeper while others were filled. Rock, glacier flour, and sand plugged the ends of many ice-dug defiles. The streams twisted and squirmed, and spilled into adjacent valleys—only to find that instead of the drainage flowing toward the Mississippi or the Saint Lawrence as before, it now flowed toward Hudson Bay.

Perhaps Babe, Paul Bunyan's Big Blue Ox, did stamp the depressions that are the little ponds and potholes of Minnesota's 10,000 lakes, but it was the great ice gouges that wrecked and tossed about towering mountains to form today's lakes in the Superior National Forest country. No hoofprint of the legendary ox could now be Lake Insula in the Roadless Area of the Superior—Insula, three miles long, half that wide, and so freckled with islands that within those dimensions are said to be 83 islets! I saw them, but I did not count them. They are little mounds above the clear waters, as if some giant had started to fill the lake by tossing fistfuls of earth here and there and then quit with the job unfinished. However they were formed, these islets and the channels between them are beautiful.

Nor could the Blue Ox have stamped and trampled enough to make the depression that holds the 55 square miles of Basswood Lake, or of Big Saganaga, or of Lac la Croix, or a dozen or a hundred other lakes, large as Basswood or small as Insula.

The colossal mass of ice that dug or dammed to make these lakes was more or less solid from the polar cap to its farthest extensions, which pushed well down toward the southern parts of what now are Ohio, Indiana, and Illinois. Five times, say the geologists, this killing ice blanket shoved out of what now is Canada. Each time the ice receded the little living things, the mosses, ferns, and lichens, began to creep back northward. In their wake the "pioneer" trees began to move up the valleys, but often the living things were again thrust back as the ice resumed its southward ploddings.

As recently as 12,000 B.C. ice sheets still covered the northern portion of the continent, so that only one small lake of the series that preceded the Great Lakes had an outlet over Niagara Falls. The major eastward flow from melting ice in 12,000 B.C. was through Canada's Ottawa River. A lake at the glacier's edge which spread near modern Toledo drained down the Maumee, and another of the same type near Chicago drained down the route of the Chicago river, both feeding into the Mississippi.

About 25,000 B.C., the ice began an over-all retreat to the north. As its southern edges alternately advanced and receded, drainage flows changed routes and directions. The west side of Lake Huron was uncovered, though the ice eastward formed a dam which backed up ice melt from that direction. The wide, crescent valley of prehistoric Grand River—which then flowed across lower Michigan and emptied this ice melt into Lake Michigan, from where it drained into the Mississippi—can still be recognized. A little later the ice shrank to uncover Green Bay and Lake Michigan drained in part from that bay by way of the Fox Valley. Still later, as ice to the eastward shrank, the drainage there was through the Finger Lakes of New York to the Susquehanna; ice still buried the Niagara River though part of Lake Michigan was ice-free. Superior still was under ice.

Though the conflicts and torsions, the thrusts and bendings to dig deep lake beds are of such proportions they merit full detailing, there is space here only to suggest the changes between this point in time and the final abandonment by the ice of the uplands north of Lake Superior. There was a span of years when the embryonic Great Lakes had three outlets; the Grand, the Susquehanna, and the Mohawk. The ice retreated, and it had another outline. A big river fed by ice melt poured along the line of the Erie Canal to cut an outlet through the Hudson's valley. These were the churning waters that excavated the roadbed for the Erie Canal. And it was at this time, while upper Michigan was still under water and today's Lake Superior began to struggle toward its present form, that the Saint Louis river "ran backwards." The river lies at the west end of the big lake. Now it runs *into* the lake at Duluth's inner harbor; but there was a period during which torrents poured in its channel to rush southwestward and join the Mississippi. In these centuries the great flow from melting glaciers was *all* down the Mississippi's channels or eastward. None of it flowed north.

In the final phase the ice cleared, and the Great Lakes outlet became the Saint Lawrence river. The immeasurable tonnage of ice that had borne down on the earth crust flowed away. The great plated cliffs of The Mountain above Hamilton, Ontario, the escarpment that is the dropoff at Niagara Falls, the "bowl edge" you see along shorelines of the upper lakes, the "lip" that is the head of Sault Ste. Marie's rapids—all tilted out of the mass of the planet. If that rim at "The Soo" were only six or seven feet higher, Lake Superior would make the Saint Louis river run backward and its waters drain down the Mississippi. At the farthest westward part of this great, slow, yawn-like action, you'll see the escarpment rising 800 feet above the business section of Duluth—the layered rock that after it rose sent most of the area's rivers scurrying *northward through the Superior National Forest, into the creeks and rivers that swell into the Winnipeg River.*

By knowing the story of this struggle, the smashing, crushing, and bending on and in the earth, you will see and recognize how we have been endowed with the maze of timber and streams and lakes of the Superior National Forest. And knowing, you then may more greatly appreciate the values of this wild area. The greatest assembly of money, men, and machines could never recreate one of the Superior's major lakes in all dimensions, materials, and beauty; only the forces and will of Creation could have shaped that lakeland forest.

As ice melted, the newly exposed land was raw and formidable. White rivers of ice melt, milky with glacial flour, spouted from under the glaciers' edges. Little plants soon began the succession of green growing things which culminates in the national forest of today.

At first only algae grew in the lakes and potholes—the simple plants related to the wavy, green "moss" and "scum" found in stagnant puddles and often the bane of those who take care of the reservoirs of a city's water-supply system. Little, mobile organisms known as "diatomes" were associates of these simple green plants. In that time the living things of the Superior forest country were unicellular, or at least simple in structures and life histories.

Soon plants of higher orders came stealing into the lake maze. Trees inched northward, straggling along the water courses as if unsure that the glaciers had actually drawn back to near the North Pole. Soils were practically without organic matter; they were mineral soils of pasty clays, sands, gravels, and often boulders. The ancestral trees, pre-glacier species, had been pushed as far south as the Ohio valley and Texas. But they finally returned.

The pioneer conifers that recaptured what was left of the Mesabi mountains were the spruces, the firs, and some jack pines. By the time they reached the Arrowhead country the lichens, mosses, ferns, and algae had begun to supply organic matter, which slowly turned the raw clays to new loam. Following the first conifers were their relatives, the white and Norway pines that were destined to make wages for lumberjacks, fortunes for many of the lumber barons— and houses for prairie farmers, too!

Why the forces of creation always work toward making earth's land masses level planes may be a mystery, but that this happens is apparent. One demonstration of this process can be seen in the lost lakes of the Superior forests. Some still are shallow ponds with central patches of clear water encircled by muskeg, rushes, and all the steadily advancing plants of these watery pastures. Other lakes have become spongy flatlands, moist, given to trembling as one tramps on the peaty masses of organic stuff that has filled them.

The paleontologists and their associated scientists worked out the story of the reforesting of the Superior; they did it by sticking a metal tube down into the old lake beds at the bottom of the bogs. The tube functioned much like a "sampler" stuck into wheat or a wheel of cheese. At the bottom of the column of stuff the tubes sampled were rock crystals, sand, gravel. The rains and wind swept up some of the "fines" left by the glaciers and spread them as a lowest layer of the lake bottoms. Above the glacial "flour" were found layers of mineral soils and fragments containing the spores of the first plants to come to the

smashed mountains; above that were the pollen grains of
the plants of higher order—among them sign of the first
conifers to creep back into the country. Layer by layer the
record of the bogs was worked out under the microscopes.
This record tells how the spruces, which were in the group
of dominant trees that first entered the Superior, were
finally choked out of many of the forest areas as the pines
grew tall, shaded the ground, and triumphed.

To us there is nothing more undisturbed than one of
these flat, treeless swamps covered with low growth and
surrounded by forest. It is placid only in terms of time.
When you look at a bog in the Superior National Forest,
you see a battlefield filled with desperate struggles.

I can tell you where you may find one of these bogs that
only yesterday was a lake and now is almost choked out of
existence. When I saw it there still was a little expanse of
open lake which now may be covered with plant growth,
with only the channel of the sluggish Dahlgren River the
remaining unsmothered water.

My first trip to the Superior National Forest was in
August of 1919. Four of us, Ranger Bert Everett, Ole Olson, then Mayor of Ely, Minnesota, Fred James, the town
clerk and a master canoeman, and myself, loaded canoes
and camp plunder on a flat push-car which trailed behind
a railway-speeder that was driven by a gasoline engine.
Olson was section boss on the D. & I.R. railway as well as
mayor. He had arranged for us to follow the logging railway
to the slab-walled camp of Swallow & Hopkins' Lumber
Company on Horse Lake. After the roller-coaster romp on
the handcar, the portages on Basswood river and around
Curtain Falls, and camping two nights on Ranger Bay of
Lac la Croix, James and I hit south to push our canoe
over the Dahlgren River route back to Ely; Olson and
Everett retraced our route along the border lakes.

Fred James was a spare, partly gray-haired man in 1919, who had spent most of his life in the north woods. I had good fortune to have such a seasoned canoeist and woods-man along on this first trip; luckily I had equally good men with me on the half-dozen other trips into the Superior and the adjacent Quetico Provincial Park of On-tario. That country demands men of this stripe, and you find them there.

Signs of moose were on all sides as James and I began our tote-paddle-and-tote trip through the wild area south of Lac la Croix. The channel of the river was almost without current; it was bordered by rank-growing grass of a type I'd seen years before in the moist meadows of western Iowa—"wild hay," we called it. Moose had fed and trampled and bedded along the banks of the river, and at one place was the sign of a fight between bulls, for the rut was beginning and the males were of a temper to attack anything that moved.

"Get that camera ready," James ordered. "Any bend we're likely to see a bull!"

Any bend—and it was the next one that we saw the bull. He was feeding. His entire head would go under the water, only the tips of his great antlers showing above the surface. He would come up with head dripping, his mouth full of the starchy roots of the yellow water lily, and before he stuck his head under for another portion he would look in all directions, raising his ugly nose and test the breeze.

"He can't see us when his head's under," James re-marked. As the bull was getting a mouthful, we had shoved the canoe into a pocket of water almost completely surrounded by high grass. "Now," continued James, "when he begins to lift his head you get low in the canoe. He's feeding this direction. The wind is blowing toward us. If he gets too close he might charge, and we're in a tight place to get out of. When I say shoot, you take that picture, and then we'll get out of here!"

Those were dragging seconds, slow-moving minutes. The bull kept coming toward us. When he raised his big head we ducked; when he nosed under we raised to watch. He was getting closer—closer.

"We can't let him get much nearer," James said, "he'll charge us if he thinks he's cornered."

My heart was pounding like a Chippewa drum. I suppose there were seconds when I held my breath. With Everett and Olson well back toward Ely on the boundary lakes, there was no other human being within hours of canoe-trailing from that grass-locked pocket where James and I crouched. This was my first moose, my first trip through a lake country so completely wilderness.

"Now—get ready," said James, huskily. "When he comes up I'll yell, and you take that picture—and we'll get the hell out of here!"

The moose raised his great head. James yelled. The moose lifted his head higher. I stood up to snap pictures. James yelled again and smacked water with his canoe paddle. There was a raveling thread of stampede in his voice. The bull looked me over thoroughly, looked to either side, and—as if there was nothing that should disturb him, as if he saw me as a fire-blackened stump—he leisurely ducked his head under and began to feed again.

But he must have decided it was no time to be caught with his antlers, ears, eyes, and nostrils under. He came up this time with his head high—'way high. In that moment I again took his picture. And James yelled again, and again, and hit the water and yelled.

"He's going to charge. Get this canoe out of here!" James shoved with his paddle so quickly that I almost pitched into the river, camera and all.

The bull had seen the movement. Slowly he began to move. He took three or four steps toward us.

"Going to charge!" James repeated. And by this time we were out of the entrapping grass pocket.

But the bull had decided he wanted none of whatever it was that was squirming around on the river with yells and waving paddles. He ran upstream and swung into the muskeg between the river and the timber. And to make sure he kept on in that direction, James took us up the river, as fast as we could paddle, chasing the big brute. He disappeared into the green timber, and we dropped our paddle rhythm to a leisurely tempo.

Just beyond the bend of the river where the bull had fed the open water narrowed. We came to a place where the tops of granite rocks protruded not more than six inches above the water level. They were at the edge of the channel; back of them for most of a mile was muskeg. Fred James knew the trickiness of this portage. The granite rocks were stepping-stones to a ledge 20 feet away beyond which rose a 10-foot granite dike that held back the water of Stuart Lake.

James braced each foot on a stepping-stone rock. They were perhaps 30 by 15 inches, but not too flat on the surface. He had picked up the paddles preparatory to swinging the canoe to his shoulders when his foot slipped.

Fred James went down to his armpits! He threw out his hands and slapped the paddles flat on the muskeg. He told me later his feet touched nothing as he hung there, kept from going entirely under by arms and paddles outspread.

That bog is a stage in the transformation of what was an open lake that is being choked day after day by the aggressive water plants, each season's increment falling to the bottom to add a new layer of black, organic mud to the many feet already deposited there. In the scale of time in

which such changes are recorded it was only a moment
ago that I saw this bog that was in a last cycle of becoming a bed of deep, rich peat. It could hardly have been
fully filled this soon, but again you might find it nearly
solid, moist land instead of the slushy muskeg with no
bottom into which Fred James sunk so spectacularly.

The sequence of change is from open lake to a "rice
lake," with its shallow, muck-filled bottom and wild rice
and reeds along the borders, to bog, and then to peat bed.
In Anoka County, Minnesota, Tamarack Lake was open
water when settlers came in there. Within man's memory
that lake has filled from a maximum depth of 41 feet to
5 feet and less; fish have frozen out; and vegetation has
almost captured the basin. The bogs of the Superior, the
lost lakes, are some of the most fascinating of all the features in the forest.

I spent the whole summer of 1919 prospecting the 23
forests in which I was to plan for recreational uses. The
one short trip in the Superior convinced me that it probably was one of the most valuable properties in the whole
national-forest system so far as human-use potentials were
concerned—the last frontier in which forests of the lake
country, the canoe trails of the Redmen and the Voyageurs,
could have sanctuary. Winter's ice had broken up only ten
days before I came back in 1921 to Ely, then the Superior's
headquarters. Rivers ran high, aspen trees were showing
only a hint of green as you viewed a whole thicket against
a cloud, and the porcupines swung perilously in the top of
the high popple branches as they filled up on fat buds and
tender bark.

Exploitation was all but charging in on this country in
1921. An industrialist of the most ruthless "Baron" type
was proposing that Canada and the United States put up
the money to build great power dams on outlets of the

magnificent border lakes. E. W. Backus, this later-day giant among exploiters of the northland, would have had the two nations build the dams, lease them to him, and he then would have sold power at retail for whatever he might garner in personal profits.

A second threat to wilderness lay in another sector.

When I came into the headquarters at Ely that summer of 1921, the supervisor of the Superior met me with bubbling enthusiasm. He was a "dry land" man; he hated water and feared it. He had been a supervisor in the western country, where roads and trails were strung throughout the forests. In the first day in the office he laid before me his road plan. He declaimed enthusiastically on how every lake would be reached by a passable road. Shorelines would be laid out in thousands of summer-home sites to be leased to the hundreds of thousands of people. Autos would dash along the roads, and the Great Quietude of the woodlands would be ruptured and rent.

Elsewhere, in my book *Timber in Your Life*, for example, the record has been told in more detail; how I returned to the regional headquarters to tell Carl J. Stahl, my regional chief, why I believed the Superior National Forest was as priceless as Yellowstone, Yosemite, or the Grand Canyon—if it remained a water-trail wilderness. I've recorded how Stahl, Paul B. Riis, and Will O. Doolittle—the latter two officials of the American Institute of Park Executives—fought against dams and roads while Sigurd Olson, who later was to lead the fight with the backing of the Izaak Walton League, and Ernest C. Oberholtzer were also calling on all the help they could muster in the locality to protect the Superior. All of these men held a thin line of defense in protecting this exquisite wilderness until help could rally to save it from internal combustion engines and humming hydroelectric turbines.

That there is now the Quetico-Superior Council, that the courts have upheld an executive order by the President allowing no intrusion of gas-driven carriers (even airplanes), that here is the one magnificent lakeland wilderness we own where you can lose yourself in wonder and vastness and beauty and reverence, that the Quetico-Superior wilderness has been and will be kept very much as the ice giants shaped it—this is what is important.

Why is it important?

I have a memory of paddling and portaging up the Kawishiwi River east of Ely, Minnesota, to the center of the roadless area. This is roadless territory rather than complete wilderness. Here we have an example of combining the highest possible type of human use with the least disturbance of full utilization of the material values the forest can supply. The shorelines appear as "virgin" timber, but in back of the belt that preserves the essence of wildlands there is planned, managed timber harvest.

Even should you hike inland from lake, stream, or portage, there will be little evidence that any part of this land is being "farmed" for timber. In a few decades at least, the relic trees, the veterans that have been able to struggle through the fires, will have served their time as seed trees and probably will have been removed; the oldest trees in the managed forest will be those younger ones left after repeated systematic thinnings. They will be ones selected to grow to sawlog size, but even they will be taken to the mills as they reach their prime. Younger trees, the next "crop," will forge ahead with more light and nutrients from the soil to mask the stumps that might be left. The forest you will see back of the natural belt along the streams will be a lusty, young, vigorous, and growing woodland. It will have its own fair countenance.

But few will hike inland. The highways are the water-

ways. Because of the policy that finally has been established
and fairly well entrenched to keep this lakeland as a wilderness sanctuary, you will see these lakes and their shores,
the life that graces this land and its waters, much as I saw
the Superior in 1919 and in subsequent years. And you will
store away such memories as the following.

I I I

OUR camp was pitched on an island in the center of Lake
Insula. Two loons began to talk beyond the open water to
the west, and I stood on the ice-smoothed rock we used
for a canoe-landing and repeated their calls. We watched
the birds, driven by curiosity, coming to investigate. Full
darkness was near when they sailed along the narrow channel between us and the next islet, thoroughly nonplused by
the silly creature on shore who talked loon language.

Another event was taking place on a near-by island. Late
that afternoon we had seen the moose cow swim out
from the mainland to the islet's sheltered bay. Wolves
would have to swim, too, if they tried to follow her to kill
the twin calves which emerged into the world that evening in 1921. We visited the new family the next morning.

"They pick that sort of location near the water," Matt
Soderback, my companion told me. "A she-moose can
stand off a pack of timber wolves if she's got water on one
side of her."

Before the last fading of afterglow on the night the
moose calves were born, two loons that seemed to be unable to hold their yelling any longer began screaming at
each other from opposite sides of Lake Insula. The first re-
flections of the stars were like flashing crystals on the dark

floor of the waters, which seemed to quiver with the rib-
ald shouting—until the loons, perhaps with linings torn
out of their throats by their vehemence, became quiet.
Then there was only the lapping of the lake and the ten-
uous sound of a wandering breeze in the pines to break the
stillness.

The next morning I lay face down, on the slight cover
of blueberry bushes, inching forward every time a cock
partridge drummed, trying to find a spot with few enough
interfering twigs through which I might take a picture
with the old, very old camera I carried. For well over an
hour I maneuvered to get that picture. I never did get it.
But a backward glance of memory's gaze can almost bring
the beat of the partridge drumming into my ears.

Another evening Matt and I sat in the motionless canoe
as a beaver who lived in Lake 1 came circling to investigate. He finally dived, slapping his tail so close to where I
sat in the bow that he spattered water on me. On the
same night Matt had looked toward the red sky where the
sun was half below the westerly edge of the visible world,
and had said that there was a large fire yonder—we learned
that there was such a fire to the west.

On another swing into the back country, we crossed
Bald Eagle Lake with 26 days' provisions in our packs to
spend the night in the small log cabin the U.S.F.S. had
built at Isabella Falls. I have heard that since 1921 Bald
Eagle Lake has had a dam across the outlet; that its shoreline now is a mess, though its out-struggling waters produce some electric current. But that evening it was a place
full of pleasant or exciting goings-on, and we were part of
the happenings. A porcupine did gymnastics in the top of
a popple tree on the south shore. When we were in the
middle of Bald Eagle Lake, a half mile from shore, we encountered a porcupine swimming—on a three-mile course

if he kept at it. He must have decided he had chosen a poor method of travel for he tried to get aboard the canoe. We had to discourage him with the flat of a paddle.

We turned into the swamp-edged inlet. Matt hissed warning and said: "There's some sort of wildlife up ahead right beside the river. Get a camera set and I'll shove the canoe up to where you can get a picture."

Matt could propel the canoe without taking the blade of the paddle out of the water. The current was sluggish, and we crept ahead, keeping heads down. Suddenly the "wildlife" took wing; a gray heron that had been spearing frogs in the swamp.

"Aw, hell!" said Matt and drove the canoe ahead with full stroke. And as we rounded the next bend—

A moose cow and calf went crashing across a little side niche in the stream bank, kicking water high. Before they were out of sight, a bull with horns in the velvet lunged across that same small arm of the river, booting water higher than his withers. Then Matt said: "Look!" He pointed to the right where a white-tail-deer doe, who surely thought she was invisible, watched us pass within ten yards of her hiding-place. She never made a move except to follow our progress with her steady gaze.

As we went up the portage around Isabella Falls, a porcupine lumbered ahead of us. During the night, beavers slapped and banged in the ponds just upstream from the cabin. Deer looking for salt stamped within ten feet of the door. The next morning we found a bear had become enraged because we had left our canoe in his path at the lower end of the portage, and he had cuffed it, sunk his teeth in the gunwale, and finally had bitten a three-inch hole through canvas and cedar planking.

For 18 days on this one trip, we saw no other human beings. The forest was rousing out of winter; each day the leafage on the aspen and popple thickets, the birches and the willows, was larger and greener. The white bloom of the ground dogwood flecked the forest floor, the native orchids nodded on their stems—and the black flies gouged little chunks of hide out of our face and hands.

The places where historical fires had run through the forest were thick with jackpine. Islands of pre-fire forest, where white and Norway pines mirrored their images in the lakes, stood high and stately. Once we surprised a young bull moose dunking for lily roots in a small pond, and he left in a fury of churned water. At another point an otter dived and dared us to try to catch him, while along another trail some large animal, which Matt thought might be one of the last remnants of the herds of woodland caribou that had lived there, crashed away in the thickets.

This was the land that the powerful industrialist wished to make ugly by fluctuating impoundments; the country that some wished to lace with auto roads. The waterways were already the grand, beckoning trails where canoes had traveled the many years before the forest was established. This is the land you may visit, the outstanding wilderness sanctuary in Region 9.

A third of a century has passed since the lines of battle were drawn between those who would assign this land to other uses and those who believed this property met its highest use if it remained "undeveloped." The Quetico-Superior probably has more safeguards to maintain the elusive qualities of wilderness than any other part of the nation. It has such protection because every thrust of the exploiters made the defenders devise protective measures against damaging the highest inspirational values in this forest.

Most of the wilderness reserves within the national forests, unfortunately, are in constant jeopardy. They were extablished only by administrative action by the Secretary of Agriculture. Legally, their "protection" is paper thin.

This being the case, there is, in fact, only an administrative "yes" or "no" between keeping these areas as wilderness and opening them to any material uses. A timber operator passing by may see trees of sawlog size. He knows a member of Congress, or a cabinet member. He starts hammering on the theme that a few "nature-lovers" are blocking "industry." It is difficult for even the most sincere custodian of our forests to stand steadfast under such pressures.

Livestock operators have had permits to graze many of the wildland reserves. In most cases they have been allowed to continue these privileges. Miners may drive a road into a wilderness reserve. They need ask no permission to prospect, sink shafts, or stake claims. If any slight color of mineral is found on these properties, roads may be forced through the center of the wilderness sanctuary.

The stock catch phrase of those who try to break into the wilderness areas is that only a few rabid "nature-lovers" ever enter these places. That is not so.

More than 60,000 people entered the roadless area in the Quetico-Superior in 1956. They paddled and portaged; they worked for the privilege of enjoying this lakeland. I would not try to put a dollar value on what they harvested in their hours of wilderness living. If someone elects to make such an evaluation, he may do this:

Assume that each of the 60,000 visitors spent an average of 5 days in the wild country of the Superior forest. That totals 300,000 man-days of human use of these reserved areas. Now apply the average per-day cost of any vacation away from home. The figure is in the millions, isn't it?

If in one year every old tree that could be economically

used were cut out of the preserved belt along lakes, streams, and portages, where they aid in maintaining the wilderness qualities, the stumpage fees might approach the dollars spent by recreation users of the Superior. But remember that 60,000 recreational visitors this or next season take away *no* materials. All those trail-side forest stands are there next year to be seen and enjoyed by another 60, or 70, or 100,000 visitors. Once the trees were cut it could be 20 to 40 years before a major harvest could be made again. Enjoyed year after year the trees left to guard the wilderness qualities are worth many times the value at any time when they may be sold as stumpage.

But I prefer the other measure of wildlands' worth, that is the help to the harried or tired or soul-hungry person in regaining faith and hope.

Bills to give legal status to these wildland sanctuaries have been introduced in Congress. One most pressing reason why they have been introduced is because, without protective legislation, these wildland reserves remain vulnerable to mining, logging, road-building, and other intrusions that would blot out their highest human-use values.

Good land-use planning would argue for the maintenance of more flexibility in shaping these wildland sanctuaries and in determining how, over the years, they may best be used. Perhaps "freezing" all the wilderness areas in our national forests will be the *only* way to keep out other damaging uses. If a bill with rigid restrictions becomes law and an absolute lock-out of all other uses follows, those who cry out against tying up even so much as we have in the wilderness reserves can blame only their own schemings to "develop" these sanctuaries.

In the last analysis it is the national forest, generally with acreage sufficient to throw a protective "buffer zone" around true wilderness, that can insure these places of far retreat. Though there are back-country wild areas in the national parks, we need such sanctuaries established in both parks and forests. They must be kept inviolate, for once there are tire tracks on them or airplane routes across them, the spell of the silent places is broken.

In Region 9 are the forest areas that will be the future tree farms, that may again produce the "cork pine"—the great lure to the loggers of the nineteenth century. In the forests in the southern parts of the region there will be a resurgence of the hardwood stands that once were the home of the passenger pigeon. None of these birds will ever return to what could be a suitable nesting habitat. In the Ozarks of both Missouri and southern Illinois, the oak-elm-yellow-poplar trees may rise on the national forests to display a token of what was swept, and rightly so, from the rich farm acres of the mid-country.

But above all, for you and me, there is the wilderness sanctuary of the Superior National Forest and its equally superb companion, the Quetico Provincial Park of Ontario, where the trails of the old voyageurs may be traversed in all the surroundings those intrepid folk found when they first entered the land, where the Mesabi mountains stood, the glaciers ground, and the waters then filled the valleys.

The first wilderness area the Forest Service designated as such was the Gila in New Mexico. Since then the pattern of this use in our national forests was hammered out, slowly, doggedly, in preserving the roadless reserves in the Superior National Forest.

IV

IN THE north-woods side of Region 9 are other forests, largely formed from the hard-beaten and burned lands of

Paul Bunyan's abandoned pineries. The 1,313,656-acre Chippewa National Forest of north-central Minnesota was named the Minnesota when I first visited it. Just as the Superior National Forest cradles many of the little ponds, bogs, and streamlets from which the flow of the Winnipeg River starts toward Hudson Bay, the Chippewa is the cradle of the Father of Waters with the flow winding aimlessly north, then east, and then determinedly south. Cass Lake with its inviting beaches of gold-tinged sands, its great old Norway pines, the walleyed-pike fishing off Star Island (shaped like a lopsided star), is one of 550 lakes in this one forest. At one time it was named officially as the source of the Mississippi. Not too well known is the fact that Pike Bay on Cass Lake is so named because in 1805–6 Zebulon Pike—whose name was given to a famous mountain—camped on this bay. Most people think the name of the bay refers to the fish.

There are 1,176 acres in natural area near Walker, Minnesota, a bit of the old pine timberland that covered most of this part of the state. Altogether, the Chippewa is a far more "gentle" forest than the Superior.

The Cheequamegnon, with a gross acreage of 1,035,000, was created out of the cut and burned lands of northern Wisconsin. To re-establish the lost forest, 96,872 acres had been planted to seedling trees by July, 1958, with over 140,000 acres still to be planted. Even by that time a calculation indicated that the annual increment of timber on this one forest amounted to 60,000,000 board feet. The lands where Bunyan and the Baron cut trees so recklessly are coming back as new forest.

In Wisconsin also is the Nicolet National Forest, containing both conifers and hardwoods. In Michigan are the Hiawatha, the Marquette, the Huron, and the Manistee forests.

Indian names are everywhere in the north woods. Lake Winnibigoshish is in the Chippewa forest. The name suggests a romantic meaning, but it means "Dirty Water." There are Chippewa names that have a more inviting meaning. In the Superior Forest there is a lake near the Ontario boundary called Kekekabic—"where-the-hawk-dwells." Ogishkemuncie is "the-lake-with-a-muskrat-channel-in-its-middle."

Just after we left Little Saganaga (which means "where-the-islands-merge-and-blend") one day, and had crossed Gabimichigami ("the lake-you-go-across"), we saw a mallard hen and her brood. As we came to the outlet where the waters poured from Gabimichigami toward Ogishkemuncie, the mallard mother with 13 downy ducklings thought she was cornered with no way to escape We tried to pull the canoe aside to let her lead the little fellows back to big water behind us, but the stream narrowed and there was an eight-foot fall below. Head-on the mallard hen drove toward that fall—and led her brood over it into the churning rapids below.

"Well," said Matt gloomily, "let's go and count the dead ducklings."

We had no chance to do that; by the time we got to a point where we could look down that channel Mother Mallard and every last duckling were racing to the lake beyond toward wide open water.

At every corner you'll encounter Indian names; you'll probably encounter Indians. You'll see the paintings on the Picture Rocks, certainly Indian made. They're located on Lac la Croix and other lakes. And if you stop at one of their villages, as Oscar and I did one time, and ask some of the Chippewas who made those paintings, they'll merely say: "The Old People did that; it was before we came to this country."

Perhaps it was the Sioux, whom we think of as plains Indians, who left those pictures. People of that Redman nation were in this area until the Chippewas were driven out of the country to the east by the advance of white settlement. Then the Chippewas drove the Sioux from the lake country and on westward to make them "Pony Indians." But who might have slapped red hands on the sheltered rocks to leave their imprint on stone, or drawn the picture stories you see on La Croix, Crooked, and other lakes with cliffs—which made such good places to leave pictographs—remains a mystery.

Other names and other history enrich a visit to the northern forests. Was the Superior's Brulé Lake named after Etienne Brulé, the Frenchman who came up the Great Lakes route the year after the Pilgrims landed? Brulé was searching for the Northwest Passage and on reaching Lake Superior he expressed his disappointment at it not being salt water. Certainly he could have camped on the lake still named Brulé.

No more engaging bit of history can be found in our country than the story of the Grand Portage. Men of the Hudson Bay and other companies tramped over the Big Lift from Lake Superior to where their canoes began to yield to the pull of the rivers starting the long run to salt water by way of Lake Winnipeg. An old treaty with England is still in effect which declares the Grand Portage shall always be open to travel by her citizens—and when that treaty was signed this was an international highway.

If you stretch on dry moss or pine needles, and watch a fire of glowing birchwood fade and wrap its last coals in gray ashes, and there is a star yonder that seems caught in the top tip of a spruce, then wonder if it is a star such as the one in the Ojibway legend.

A young man, hurrying toward his tribe's village late

one night, saw a star caught in a spruce tree. It looked so lovely that he climbed up to lift it from its couch on a feathery spruce twig so he might take it home. But as he reached the ground again, the star in his grasp became a beautiful young woman—a Star Goddess.

Of course, they fell in love; they married; and there were fine children. But the Red Gods called the girl to return to her place in the sky. She refused. The gods, angry perhaps, but still with a bit of compassion, transformed this Star Goddess into the water lily—and as the star-shaped flower opens its face in the evening, the girl who was a star and then a flower, is in the company of her own people, their images around her projected to the mirror of the darkened waters.

Or you might see the exquisite white water lily in one of the pools or bays in these northern forests of ours and remember how that flower came to earth. The star or the flower you might see with many other lovely things if you were to visit one of these more northern forests of Region 9.

You'll not meet Paul Bunyan there, nor the Timber Baron. They've gone west.

V

THE NUMBER ONE REGION

I

BECAUSE millions of her acres are covered by pure stands of lodgepole pine, Montana could have rightfully claimed it as her state tree. But it was Wyoming that adopted that pine as her green symbol; Montana, the hub state in Region 1 of the U.S. Forest Service chose the ponderosa pine.

Trees have personalities. The ponderosa pine is an aristocrat, both in its full maturity as a tree and when, as lumber, its wood weathers to a rich, sunny brown. In its youth ponderosa is gregarious. Juvenile trees group in well-ordered broods beneath hovering limbs of their elders. But old ponderosas often stand alone, as if they insist on being individuals.

Lodgepole is more like a member of the common rabble. A typical lodgepole stand is usually a forest tenement, its residents all crowded to a point of jostling each other. This pine is a tough, assertive tree that fights fiercely for its food and drink. The toughness of lodgepole, expressed in another way, is proven by those great, undulating carpets of yellowish green forest draped across miles of Montana's mountains.

Fire kills the seed of most trees. The phoenix-like lodgepole rushes in to pre-empt burned-over land. Fire's heat spreads the bracts of the pebble-hard, plum-size cones so the paper-winged lodgepole seeds are released. "The Great

[133]

Fire of 1910" prepared the way for much of the rug-like covering this pine supplies to Region 1's mountains.

Other trees of considerable worth are found in Region 1. Among them are a brace of true firs, and the odd fellow among the evergreens known as Douglas fir (which isn't a fir and has the technical name, *Pseudotsuga taxifolia*, meaning "the false hemlock with needles like the yew tree"). The Englemann spruce—named after German-born George Englemann, physician, botanist, and meteorologist, who lived in Saint Louis after settling there in 1832—drapes miles-wide wreaths around Montana's higher mountain sides. The true western red cedar, which is a close relative of our home gardens' arborvitæ and the western hemlock, are additional forest residents. In the stream bottoms are the cottonwoods, aspens, and alders.

Region 1 is wide-flung across our farthest north Rockies, across their spurs and outflanking hills. The farthest east portions of the region's subdivisions are parts of the Custer: 78,000 acres of this national forest are in South Dakota. The western parts of the Custer shove in against the Gallatin forest, which shares its southern boundary line with the northern boundary of Yellowstone National Park. All of Montana is in Region 1; the U.S.F.S. headquarters is at Missoula. The national forests of Idaho which lie north of the Salmon River are in this region, and so are two forests in the northeastern corner of Washington.

This region acquired the number "1" because of its position on the map and the period in which its boundaries were drawn. Had we been entirely subservient to system, this region might have appeared first in this book, but it seemed more reasonable to begin in the northeastern part of the country and, step by step, progress toward the western edge of the nation—somewhat in the sequence the lumber industry invaded the virgin woods.

The first forest reserves were those proclaimed where there still was suitable public land available to be set aside. The national forests' growth is one great movement that expanded from west to east, and thus against the usual westward current of settlement and development. The national-forest idea was seeded in the east, but it sprouted and grew to size in western soils.

So when the time came to delegate authority from the Washington offices and bring administration closer to the field by organizing regions, the existing forests were almost wholly in the 11 "public land" states. Beginning then with Region 1 in the northern Rockies, the numbering of the first regions to be set up is clockwise, south from Region 1, west, then North to Region 6, which contains most of Washington and Oregon.

I I

THE mountains and forests of Region 1 are parts of our Rocky Mountains. These are young mountains. Their heights were thrust up just prior to our most recent Ice Age—the one during which all known human residence on earth has occurred.

Long, long ago, before these young mountains rose to become the Rockies, there was an ancient range that stood approximately where this continental backbone now stands from Canada to Mexico. This early system of mountains was worn down until there were only the core-rock nubs of the old peaks showing above the peneplane formed from wreckage of the older heights. A period followed in which a shallow, brackish inland sea covered this part of the earth. The waters laid layer after layer of mud under the sea. The muds became stone. Along the eastern edge of the Rockies' foothills are great tilted and broken plates of limestone and sandstone that once lay flat beneath this arm of the oceans. Some of this sedimentary rock was even lifted to the tops of higher mountains as the new Rockies bulged and boiled out of the planet's center. The mere fact that the tops of many heights of the Rockies are such softer stone is evidence of the youth of these mountains. In older mountain ranges erosion has stripped away the softer mantle from the hard, heat-fused core rock.

The rivers and their tributaries supply more evidence that our Rockies are new. The streams tumble and brawl out of the high valleys where still are found occasional decadent glaciers. These dwindling ice masses are remnants of more or less continuous ice caps that spread over the heights with arms thrusting out and down to plow out U-shaped canyons.

The tumbling streams of the Rockies are busily gnawing away at rock and rubble to make their courses deeper. If there will be men to see these newer mountains ages hence, these cascading waters may have again completed the erosion cycle, and a peneplane will spread where peaks now rear.

The important fact to us is that the Rockies we see to-day are rough, high, and young.

Among the geological features in this region is a telling example of how great the earth's travail may sometimes be. It is located in Glacier National Park and southward in the Lewis & Clark and Flathead National forests. In New Hampshire's White Mountains a great sheet of earth crust shoved upward, over, and slid toward the west. In these Montana heights a mighty horizontal landslide slipped over just such prairie land as lies out from the park in the Blackfeet Indian Reservation. The escarpments facing east in the park are the exposed edges of this block of plains that snapped up to slide eastward for 22 miles.

Region 1 offers many more geological features that merit attention. Minerals lace through the ribs of the mountains: gold, silver, copper, and others that were boiled through fractured rocks as mountains rose. Canyons, pinnacles, rim-rocks, and many other mountain features may be visited and their stories read.

The Shoshones, Blackfeet, Bloods, Crows, Crees, Pigans, and other Indians lived and fought to live in the great valleys of this region. Here are probably a few of the very limited places where you might see the awing Sun Dance ceremonies without adulteration by Chamber of Commerce promotions. Though it was some years ago when I paid my most recent visit to the Sun Lodge of the Shoshones, recollections of the solemn and ancient rites remain vivid.

The Indians who had invited us to their Sun Dance had come to their traditional campground in trucks, automobiles, lumber wagons, and on horseback. The stately group of the conical tepees (in these later days covered with canvas instead of hides) was broken here and there by the ordinary wall tent of the whiteman, but it was entirely an Indian camp.

Campfires flickered where meals were being prepared, and friends sat and related to each other what had transpired since they had gathered here the year before. As they talked, there was the flicker of hands, like constantly moving bird wings, or wind-flurried leaves. Always these signs duplicated the words. The old people of these tribes give drama to their speech by blending their two languages, spoken and sign.

At the far side of the tent-rimmed circle of the camp was the Sun Lodge. Earlier in the day we had watched the lifting of the center pole with its song and symbolism. At the top of the center pole were the white and the blue flags, the eagle skin fastened so the beak pointed to the east, the buffalo head placed so it faced the west. We had seen 11 of the 12 units of the round lodge sides filled in with cottonwood saplings all leafy and green. From the lodge, where those who had made a vow to dance this year were fulfilling their pledge, came the drum beats. As constant as the throb of the drum was the song of the musicians and the "peep-peep-peep" of the feather-decked whistles made of bones from an eagle's wing. The drumming, the singing, the jerky "peep" blown by each dancer as he crow-hopped, eyes toward the symbolic center pole, would continue throughout three nights and two days—without any dancer receiving food or water.

Hope, if you can, that some Indian friend may sense you regard his Sun Dance as a solemn religious observance instead of a show, and that he will invite you as we were invited to be a visitor to such an encampment. Then, somewhere in these eastern portions of the Rockies, in the belt that is part plains, part mountains, from where the Bloods of Canada dwell to far down into the Ute homeland of southwestern Colorado, you might be honored and fascinated as you view this ceremony.

Indian days are a great, shimmering backdrop against which we view the later history of this region. Redmen watched long covered-wagon trains lumbering westward, the people with them hurrying toward farms or gold camps. Vigilantes once ruled Virginia City, which stands in the valley between divisions of the Beaverhead National Forest. There they hung Joe Slade, the one-time Pony Express man.

More names of places and of topographic features reach out from maps and capture your attention, such as these:

East of Butte, south of Helena, west of Bozeman, near the point where U.S. 10 splits into 10N and 10S to join again at Garrison, Montana, is a modest valley town named Three Forks. On Saturday, July 27, 1805, a man named Clark was camping with companions near this spot. He was having a miserable time with mosquitos and a bilious attack. Chills and fever racked him, and he was in pain. On the advice of his partner, Meriweather Lewis, Clark took a good dose of Rush's pills and soaked his feet in hot water. That, said Lewis, would cure the illness. It did, for Clark was well enough the next day to enter into a discussion as to whether or not any of the three streams that came together at that point in Greater Louisiana should continue to be called the Missouri river, or something else.

Since all of these streams were about equal in size, the decision was that each deserved a separate name. The southwesterly one was called the Jefferson after the "projector of the enterprise" that Clark and Lewis were on. The middle fork was named the Madison to honor James Madison, then Secretary of State, while the third branch was called the Gallatin, surname of Mr. Jefferson's Secretary of the Treasury.

And it was here also that a few years earlier Sacajawea, spouse of Toussaint Chaboneau, had first seen the Minnetarees who made her prisoner and took her to the land of the Mandans. There she was sold to the French trapper Chaboneau and became his wife. The lazy Chaboneau joined the Lewis and Clark expedition as interpreter, but it was Sacajawea who guided the party and shared the fame of that great adventure with its leaders.

The three rivers that come together to fuse into the Missouri still hold the titles given that summer day in 1805. All receive their waters from timbered basins within Region 1's national forests. Probably at no other one spot is there such a full gathering of so many place names that were bestowed by those who explored the west during the first few years after our nation had made the Louisiana Purchase.

Many animals, birds, and fishes met within forests of Region 1 are first mentioned in the Lewis and Clark journal. The prairie dogs, the gophers, and the magpies were tallied along with the buffalo, antelope, wapiti, and mule deer. While camped at the Great Falls of the Missouri, the explorers caught their first Rocky Mountain white fish. Here also the first cutthroat trout of record was caught and described; the cutthroat's scientific name is *Salmo lewisii*.

The Yellowstone river delays its joining with the Missouri until both reach the boundary line between Montana and North Dakota. Before they reached this junction members of the Lewis and Clark expedition had seen the great white bears later called grizzlies. At the time the beasts seemed more interested in beating a retreat than engaging in battle. But at eight o'clock one morning, as he was hunting near the streams' junction, Meriweather Lewis and his companion came face to face with two of these great beasts.

Lewis shot at one bear, the hunter at the other. Both animals were wounded. One ran away. The other charged at Captain Lewis. The Captain ran. While running he managed to reload his rifle and fire. The great "white bear" fell.

It would seem a great absurdity to Captain Lewis and

his associates that in the Lewis and Clark National Forest, just south of Glacier National Park, Montana, there is a refuge to preserve the great "white bear" from extinction.

No region of the Forest Service presents such a variety in hunting and fishing as this one. Here you may angle for grayling and cutthroat trout, salmon and white fish and sturgeon. Brants and dusky grouse, antelope and white tail deer, moose, mountain goats, elk, bears, and bighorns are legal game in season. Except where there are designated wildlife refuges, the almost 28,000,000 acres of national forests in Region 1 provide some of the best hunting and fishing in the United States.

Perhaps one of the most significant hours of Indian history was marked when Chief Joseph of the Nez Percé tribe finally surrendered in October of 1877 to General Miles. The Indians under Joseph's leadership had fought off and outwitted the U.S. Army all the way from Oregon to Montana. General Gibbon's troops had killed warriors, their women, and their children in the surprise attack on the Indians at Big Hole. The end of this war trail for Joseph's tribe was at a point near the Bear's Paw Mountains of the national forest of that name. One of Region 1's other large forests, located in southern Idaho, is named the Nezperce.

In that same year another man, John Wesley Powell, who sought neither peltry, gold, or grazing-land, traced his way through Montana. This man asked thoughtful questions of the soils and waters in Region 1, and they revealed their secrets to him. Long ago Powell foretold that plowing the prairies where precipitation was less than 20 inches yearly would lead to dust storms. He also forecast how irrigation waters if spread on the unleached soils of the semi-arid west, would become so loaded with alkali salts that crops planted on them will sicken and die.

It is a strange commentary that Powell's sage advice has been repeated so many times by men of science and disregarded by those who stubbornly try to make nature conform to their wishes, striving to make the western soils perform like Illinois's mellowed farm land. In their blind striving these human beings become the producers of dust bowls of the dryland farm communities and the poisoners of irrigated fields.

For those who wish to pursue the historical trails, there are many more places to be visited, and there are printed pamphlets or local legends to guide one. But nowhere in one volume will you find all that could be recorded about "The Great Fire" of 1910.

III

PERSONS still live who remember how the forests flamed during The Great 1910 Fire. I remember something about that fire. I was a high-school student, and during those flame-laced days in Montana I never was outside of Monona County, Iowa, but I remember how the glowering red sun went down behind the loess hills flanking the Maple Valley and how, if you sniffed the air, you recognized the pungent taint of wood smoke in it. Twelve hundred miles away we had these signs of the fires burning in the woods "out in Montana." Where those fires burned there was terror, heroism, and heartbreak.

We cannot ignore that fire. Across the hills where the forests of Region 1 are spread are marks it left as it streamed from west to east on a front that was from 20 to 35 miles wide for a distance of 120 miles. It burned over most of that area in a space of 24 hours.

Historic fires have visited their destruction on many sections of the wildlands. The all-time apex of forest-fire disaster was the Pestigo, Wisconsin, fire in October 1871. It leaped alive only a few hours ahead of the Chicago fire, and perhaps its devastation was slightly overshadowed by the fire in the city. At Pestigo brush fires that had been burning innocuously for days suddenly were fanned to life by the winds, joined into one big front, and before the flames subsided an estimated 1,500 people were killed and 1,250,000 acres of forest were burned.

At the same time the Pestigo fire flamed another burned 2,000,000 acres of forest lands in the Manistee and Au-Sable Valleys of Lower Michigan. Ten years later much the same area was burned with a loss of 169 lives. In 1894 the Hinkley, Minnesota, fire dealt death to 418 people and burned great patches of north-woods timber. And at Cloquet, Minnesota, in 1918, 250,000 acres burned and 453 people died.

Not so many died in The Great 1910 Fire of Region 1 as in those other fires; there were only 85 known dead. But it exceeded those landmark fires of the midlands in acreage burned and is one of the Forest Service's most historic conflagrations. This particular fire was more like an explosion than a normal forest fire.

Throughout the summer of 1910 the clouds that came sailing toward the northern Rockies continually promised good, soaking showers. Rain did not come; fire did. From early summer crews were repeatedly racing into the rough, pathless back country—of which there is much in Region 1—to squash little fires. Often these had grown to dangerous dimensions before men on foot or riding horseback and leading pack animals could get the crew and equipment to where timber burned.

By mid-August these weary crews, led by rangers even

more fatigued, had gone into remote canyons and across rough ridges to beat down 3,000 small fires. Fire lines that were trenches and cleared belts had been grubbed out around 100 big fires. On August 18 all these were supposedly, "under control." Smoke kept rising from within the fire lines, but it was lazy smoke, from embers that were sleeping. This was the situation on the night of August 18, 1910. There was no change at dawn on the 19th. It promised to be merely another August day, hot, perhaps, and droughty, but uneventful.

Then came the combination all forest men fear. The humidity dropped toward zero. A wind out of the southwest began to build higher and higher. It took on hurricane force. Suddenly the whole sky to the west of the Bitterroot and Coeur d'Alene Mountains, which flank out from the boundary between Montana and Idaho, filled with smoke. A yellow glare mounted into the hot sky. Fire lines were abandoned, and men ran for their lives. The fires that had been "under control" seemed to splash over the feeble barriers that had held them. Their red waves joined until all rolled over the sides of the hills like a tidal wave.

The Rangers in charge of the crews had only one thought: get the men out alive!

Ranger Pulaski, a descendant of the famous Pole who came to fight on the side of the Colonies during the American Revolution, had a 150-man crew on a ridge between the Big Creek tributary of the Coeur d'Alene River and the Big Creek that feeds into the St. Joe River. The crew was suddenly trapped by a "big blow-up" of encircling fire.

Pulaski knew of an old mine tunnel, 150 feet long, that could be reached before the fire closed in. He led his men and two horses toward this haven. One man didn't make it. At the tunnel Pulaski ordered the men back from the entrance while he remained to scoop up water that drained out from seeps back in the tunnel and throw it on the timbers holding back loose earth above and at the sides of the entrance. If these timbers burned and the earth caved in, the tunnel would become a death trap.

Pulaski finally collapsed. He remained unconscious while the fire swept by. Five men in the tunnel suffocated. The two horses were so badly burned they had to be shot. One of Pulaski's crew finally got through to Wallace, Idaho, a rescue party was formed, and those who still lived were taken to safety.

In more than one camp, rangers in charge of fire crews drew belt guns and promised quick, sure death for any who would not obey commands. John W. Bell's crew, which had been working in conjunction with Pulaski's, took refuge in a two-acre clearing on the John Beauchamp homestead. Seven men thought a root cellar was a safe place, but the timbers of that man-built cave caught fire, and all within died. Others lay down in the stream close by, but three were killed there by falling trees. Many who followed Bell's orders and did survive had all the hair burned off the back of their heads and necks.

All through the hills as the red tide of flame rolled and roared that day men cowered in whatever shelter they could find. They hid in mine tunnels, found clearings and lay flat, or they threw wet blankets over their heads and crouched in creeks and rivers. At one camp two men went mad. One regained his sanity, the other never did. Only the commands of cool-headed crew foremen saved the many lives that did survive that storm of fire.

In that one day the fire swept a pathway 120 miles long, destroying 8,000,000,000 board feet of standing timber on 3,000,000 acres. Then rain came.

I V

FEW trails and fewer roads over which fire crews could travel into the rough, tough back country of Region 1 were available in 1910. Extensive areas in this region have no auto highways through them. They remain the most isolated forest areas in the continental United States. But there is a new campaign plan for fire control, fashioned in part by forest people in this region, which illustrates how far the U.S. Forest Service has advanced in meeting the fire threat and squelching each blaze before it becomes big and dangerous.

Though the use of the airplane was pioneered in other regions as well as in Region 1, Missoula, Montana, became the headquarters of that seemingly daredevil legion, the Smoke Jumpers.

Like hawks, these young, highly conditioned, thoroughly trained men soar over a fire far in the back country and parachute from planes to grapple with a fire just beginning to spread on the ground below. This action would seem reckless. It actually is coldly calculating. Back of each jump are hours on hours of testing, planning, and training. This pre-jump preparation has kept the accidents to Smoke Jumpers at a minimum.

As evident as it must have been that chutes could carry men swiftly to small fires, the Forest Service seemed hesitant about organizing such shock troops. These dates mark steps in organizing the aerial fire suppression teams:

1925—Forest Inspector Howard R. Flint with the assistance of Lieutenants Nick Mamer and R. T. Freng, Air Force Reserve, organized an aerial fire patrol at Spokane, Washington, and took aerial photos.

1929—First cargo drop to a fire crew.

1934—J. B. Bruce, a professional, demonstrated a jump in Region 4, to show how a few fire-fighters might arrive and block the flames before the blaze became large.

1939—Experimental jumps by professionals and Forest Service personnel began in the Chelan National Forest of Washington. It was demonstrated that chutists could land in timber if properly equipped.

1940—A small force of Smoke Jumpers was organized in both Region 1 and Region 6 directly west of Region 1. The Region 1 crew made jumps to nine "selected" fires. The first actual jump to a fire with the idea of controlling it was on July 12, 1940, in the Nezperce National Forest—not far from where The Great Fire of 1910 roared. Those making the jump were Rufus Robinson of Koosia, Idaho, and Earl Cooley, of Hamilton, Montana, and they landed on Martin Creek.

In jumping to control the nine "selected" fires, it was reckoned that the cost was about $30,000 less than what it would have cost to control these by employing trucks, pack trains, and back-packs on men. There was another spur to keep smoke-jumping developing swiftly. War had broken out in Europe. The Smoke Jumpers of R-1 became pioneers in trying out techniques that suddenly became of highest importance if paratroopers were to be trained. One visitor to the Smoke Jumper headquarters was Major William Gary Lee, who soon organized the first paratroops that trained at Fort Benning, Georgia. Lee later headed the First Airborne Division, which went in the day the Allies hit the beaches of Normandy.

In 1941 the Smoke Jumper headquarters for the nation was established in Region 1. During the war men with religious scruples against killing other human beings took over the smoke-jumping and proved both their loyalty and courage. In 1952, 362 jumps were made in Region 1. It was reckoned that in the one region these tactics saved a net of $155,000. Something of a peak was reached in 1953 when 994 jumps were made to 236 fires.

During that year 30 tons of treated timber for lookout towers and 200 tons of supplies for fire-fighters in addition to the Smoke Jumpers' standard light equipment were delivered by "para cargo." Some additional tons of materials and supplies for back-country construction were delivered by parachute.

Visiting the Smoke Jumper headquarters is similar to entering a blend of college campus and alert military installation. The jump crews are the athletes; many of them work at smoke-jumping to keep in condition so later they can "make" college teams. But back of these fellows who bail out over rough country with a prayer and fire tools is an elite organization. For example, each jumper's chute pack has been minutely examined, checked for weakness or damage, and then ever so carefully packed by men who know a life may be endangered by any poorly laid fold.

In another work room are the primary hand tools the Smoke Jumper must have when he grapples with fire. Among these there may be a small portable pump and long hose, which can utilize a water supply in a lake or a little creek. Certain big metal containers with thick, insulated sides can be hooked to a chute and dropped, and when the crew flips the lid on these, they find packaged hot dinner ready to serve.

A call comes through reporting a fire in back country. Alarms ring. Loud-speakers talk. The men who are called hike to the ready room. They don padded suits, helmets with face protectors similar to a baseball catcher's mask, and two chutes. Meanwhile the whole array of equipment, including, in some cases, paper sleeping-bags that can be disposed of in far back country, is being loaded into the drop plane. The record has been set at much shorter time, but it takes an *average* of 20 minutes from the moment the call for the Smoke Jumpers comes in and the time of the take-off of the plane.

Lookouts, aerial observers, and other reporters have told where the smoke has started to rise. The plane comes in above the fire for a reconnaissance. A target for the drop of men and equipment is chosen. Usually there are little meadows for cargo drops and perhaps some good, bushy trees at the edge of the grassy places for men to land in. A technique of using the branches of a spruce or fir to land in has been developed which is easier and safer than hitting open ground.

The plane comes in again, releasing miniature parachutes to test wind drift. The drop run is governed by quick calculations made after that test. The men jump, the parachutes open, they guide their chutes to a comfortable-looking tree, and as soon as they hang up there they flip and zip out of their harness, loop the light, strong rope they carry over a limb, slide to the ground, and hurry to the spot where the cargo chutes are delivering equipment. It may be only minutes, in fact, before one of the Smoke Jumpers has put the portable radio outfit in operation and is reporting to headquarters that a safe landing has been made, an appraisal of the fire completed, and crew men are already choking out the flames.

Region 1 is pioneering in other directions to aid in fire control. High-frequency radios are replacing the old-style Ranger Station telephone lines that have a habit of going out of business at the first lightning from thunderstorm. The stationary telephone supplied an estimated 1 per cent coverage in reporting fires. With the forest-wide high-frequency installations 60 per cent complete on the Saint Joseph National Forest, the radio with its mobility covered an estimated 75 per cent.

Region 1 also has been experimenting with modern cloud-seeding procedures with the idea of modifying lightning hazards. Years may pass between the start of this project, dubbed "Skyfire," and the practical use of cloud-seeding to break up fire-setting lightning storms, but results may come swiftly. Currently, the first steps are being taken in using helicopters to hover in over a small fire and spray fire-extinguisher chemicals from a small nozzle. This opens an entirely new way to halt a destroying forest fire.

This is a glimpse at fire control as it is now organized in the country where fire ran high, wide, and terrifying on August 19, 1910.

V

HISTORICALLY fire has been the worst enemy of the forests. Times have changed. The greatest damage to our timber today is visited on it by a far less spectacular enemy than fire.

The "Little Destroyers"—insects and organisms lumped together under the general term "diseases"—cause losses in forests and in the wood that they produce which are greater by 50 per cent than losses by fire.

The destruction wrought is not as spectacular as that wrought by fire. Some of these destructive organisms are so small they require a high-powered microscope to be seen. The bacteria, the thready fungi, and some tiny one-celled animals work their havoc slowly and in hidden zones of the trees. Sometimes not until trees die is there warning that these killers are running loose.

In recent years insect damage in forests of Region 1 have been as menacing as fires were in 1910. You may see patches of spruces and pines in Region 1 that are brown, almost as if seared by flame, with no evidence of fire having passed that way. Or you may see twigs that have lost all needles and are bare. Most likely you are looking at the work of tree-destroying beetles.

Probably nobody can say how many kinds of these pigmy killers prey on trees and wood. Though there might be an approximation on Monday, by the following Friday, a fungus, an insect, or a bacterium that had been helpful or at least non-harmful might have switched to the destructive group. These small killers do damage in our national forests at least one and one half times as great as that caused by fire.

Do not minimize fire. In 1952, for example, it is credited with destroying 781,000,000 board feet of saw timber. But in the same year, disease destroyed nearly 2,500,000,000 board feet of saw timber, and insects destroyed over 5,000,000,000 board feet. This was in commercial forests of all types. The losses from, and the programs to control, the inroads of insects and diseases are grouped on Forest Service work sheets under the heading "I & D."

Several areas and types of attack on the forests of Region 1 are in this "I & D" category. White-pine blister rust is one of the diseases. It has damaged thousands of trees, many thousands, in eastern states as well as in the west. One campaign in Region 1 well illustrates how the U.S.F.S. fights these small destroyers.

The white-pine blister rust is a fungus. It was brought to the North American continent in shipments of pine-tree seedlings from Europe. First identified at Geneva, New York, in 1906, it had spread by 1915 far and wide throughout New England and adjacent territory. In 1921 it was found in the Pacific Northwest, brought in again by a shipment of small pines, this time from Europe to Vancouver, B.C.

This fungus attacks only the "5-needle pines." Any species of our eight trees in the white-pine group is susceptible. It may take 30 years for this fungus to kill an older tree, but in the tender tips of young pines it can defoliate the tree and invade the cambium with the seedling being killed in a season or two.

The spores of this fungus are released as they become "ripe" in the minute cavities the fungus has forced into pine needles or tender, new bark and can be borne by a breeze only about 900 feet on the average. Then the spore must find an "alternate host" to perform the next steps of the blister rust's life cycle. That alternate host must be a *Ribes*—a currant or gooseberry or one of their blood relatives. The fungus *must* spread from pine to *Ribes*, then back, never from pine to pine. Here is the vulnerable spot in the life history of the white-pine blister rust. If it is unable to find bushes of any of the currant family to fasten on, then the spore has reached the road block for that particular infestation.

By 1950 the campaign to eradicate all of the wild currant and gooseberry bushes in the white-pine territory of Region 1 had cost a neat $2,250,000. The members of the currant family had been grubbed out of only 63,000 acres where western white pine is an important forest tree, and that was less than half the acreage in which Region 1's 5-needle pine stands are important.

In 1955 there were eight camps with a total of 250 men located in national forests of Region 1 busily grubbing out the currant bushes and their relatives. There were two other camps, with 80 men on the job, that were state and private currant-eradication units.

There are about 26,000,000 acres of land in the United States on which white pine is of prime importance. The first task of yanking out all currant and gooseberry bushes was completed by 1950 on 14,000,000 acres, so only maintenance was required thereafter.

I wonder if some hunter, combing the woods for a shot at grouse which had been plentiful in the area in former years, has any inkling that the scarcity of these game birds might be caused by the uprooting and burning of *Ribes* bushes—and that the instigator of the destruction of this bird food was a tiny little tree-killer that sneaked into the country in some bundles of white-pine seedlings.

There are some 300 species of fungus which are known to use wood in some form as a host. Many are beneficial and many are indifferently destructive, but when fungi kill timber as has the white-pine blister rust, men must regard them as thieves of the first rank.

The white-pine-blister-rust campaign in Region 1—in an area we do not usually think of as white-pine territory—the potential and actual losses and costs to control this introduced disease, indicate, in general, the battle that must be waged against destructive fungi and their kind.

But the fungus is typical of only the "D" part of the "I & D" battles. Often the "I" portion is even more destructive than the diseases.

An introduced destructive disease or insect may be far more damaging than those that are long residents of our woodlands. The introduced organism usually leaves behind in its former home all its natural enemies. It runs unchecked for a time. Our native insects and diseases that damage the forests usually do have some enemies or checks that keep them from running rampant. But occasionally these native pests explode and run riot.

A family of "bark beetles" named *Dendroctonus*—which is a derivation from the Greek and means "tree-killer"— has inflicted some of the most spectacular losses in our western forests.

Between 1895 and 1908 *Dendroctonus ponderosa* plagued the ponderosa-pine forests of South Dakota's Black Hills. It killed practically all of those pines growing on 100,000 acres. The same beetle invaded the Kaibab Plateau north of the Grand Canyon in Arizona, and between 1917 and 1926 killed 12 per cent of all the yellow pine trees in the area.

A bark beetle struck at the lodgepole pines in Idaho and Montana in the 1920s, increasing the fire potential as well as killing trees.

The most shocking record of recent losses from these beetles occurred in Colorado between 1939 and 1951. In that span of years an epidemic of *Dendroctonus englemanni*, which preys primarily on the Englemann spruce, began in southwestern Colorado in a tangle of trees blown down and half dead. It fanned out across the state and killed an estimated 4,000,000,000 board feet of timber before it subsided. Nearly a fourth of Colorado's standing timber was killed. Five national forests had browning trees, not in patches but in whole sweeping zones that blanketed mountain side after mountain side. Before adequate federal funds were appropriated, before natural checks surged up to help forest crews, this beetle was on its way to kill some additional 10,000,000,000 board feet of timber, and perhaps sweep into other states north and south along the main range of the Rockies.

This is the beetle, the spruce bark beetle, that showed up in force soon after 1950 in Region 1. The shadow of entire spruce forests being killed hung over Region 1. It threatened among many timber stands old spruce just north of the Bob Marshall Wilderness Area. North of this infestation was Glacier National Park. In that location beetles could move into both the park and the wilderness area.

Though there were equally bad beetle attacks in other parts of the forests, this particular one became an issue. Should a truck road be allowed which might get "beetle crews" into the wilderness so trees could be sprayed? Should "brood trees" be cut and wood in them salvaged?

Many words were said and written about this particular "bug area." The shadow of a build-up such as had occurred in Colorado's national forest seemed to hover menacingly over the spruce of the wilderness area and adjacent forests, including those in Glacier National Park.

Essentially, the sweep of a beetle epidemic is comparable to that of a fire. The main difference lies in the speed with which the destruction is accomplished. It is doubtful if anyone would have questioned putting fire crews inside the wilderness area. But, for some reason, beetle kill seemed vastly different. A season or two passed and there was no problem. Practically all of the trees that would be attacked by beetles had been invaded. Such bugs as would spread to other areas had done so. Some natural checks had begun to develop.

This beetle and its kin, as is the case with most of the native insect pests and diseases, are endemic in the forests. Every now and then they have explosive increases. Conditions shape so that a tremendous brood stock builds up, and the species runs destructively wild.

When not on a rampage these beetles were the "loggers" of natural woodlands. If they are present in epidemic numbers, they may attack young, lusty trees, but generally it is the old, declining tree that attracts them. One means of control is based on this trait of the beetles. They seem to know when a tree is dying. Some forest men suspect the beetles detect this by some "smell" of wood in the first stages of decay. As one phase of beetle control, trees are cut in the autumn, and the logs are left near the truck roads so the men can get to them easily. Beetles swarm into these "trap trees." Next spring the bark is skinned off, the beetle larvae exposed, so it will die, the bark burned.

The spruce bark beetle that can create such havoc is black, about a quarter of an inch long, and normally has a two-season life cycle. A pair of adult beetles on their "mating flight" alight at the base of a spruce tree. They enter the bark, bore into the cambium, and there the female lays eggs in tiny tunnels branching on either side of the more or less vertical corridor she and her mate gnaw through the cambium.

The eggs hatch in three to four weeks. The larva is a little white "grub"—this is the killer. It does not tunnel the cambium on a vertical line but horizontally, around the tree. An infested spruce may have many thousands of such channels cut around the trunk and in its cambium layer. Though the tree is as completely girdled as it would be by cutting around it with an ax, for a time it continues to appear green and healthy.

The grubs feed until autumn, become dormant during the winter, feed a little again in the spring, and then move on from the larval stage to the pupal form, which then becomes the adult beetle. The adults may spend a little more time feeding. They may remain just under the bark of the tree, which now begins to show symptoms of being a "beetle tree." Or the beetles may leave the inner bark of the tree and congregate under plates of rough bark at its base. Next summer the paired beetles leave this tree and begin their "nuptial flight" to a new tree. The male begins to bore upward inside the outer bark, the female follows to lay her eggs where the side galleries will be cut by the larva, and the cycle starts all over again.

The older method of trying to stop an epidemic was to cut down the trees and slash off the bark and burn it. A variation of this sort of approach is the "trap tree." The big Colorado epidemic was stopped, however, by sending scores of "beetle crews" into the field. The men were equipped with hand-powered knapsack-type spray outfits. An oil-base liquid with insecticide was sprayed at the foot of each infested tree before the brood from that particular spruce began the nuptial flight. A more penetrating spray was also developed that reached into the galleries and killed the larvae there. But the costs of spraying are high.

Normally one of the greatest controls of this beetle is killing cold, which freezes grubs under the bark. Also, should beetles try to invade a healthy tree the abundant flow of resinous sap generally drowns them. They are more definitely killers of over-mature trees. That is a key to future beetle control; to have over mature trees so well harvested that there will be no preferred hosts available.

But the last word in control comes from the birds and a particular small wasp.

Three woodpeckers of the western uplands do their very large bit in handling this beetle. The birds are western species of the downy, the hairy, and the alpine woodpeckers. Given a chance to build up their forces, they are potent beetle destroyers.

The greatest enemy of the spruce bark beetle is a little wasp, not a half inch long. This tiny wasp carries the pretentious name of *Coeloides dendroctoni*. As physicians will refer to a medicine as a "specific," in that it is a cure for one particular malady, so the little wasp is a "specific," in that it cleans up infestations of *Dendroctonus engle-manni.*

The female wasp has a proportionally very long oviposi-tor. She lights on a beetle tree and unerringly drives that ovipositor through the bark and *into* a beetle grub. There she lays her egg and there hatches the larva of the wasp, inside the grub larva of the beetle—next spring, no grub; just a little wasp that has eaten on beetle larva all winter.

In one instance, the wasps and the woodpeckers moved into one whole Colorado mountain range that was on the verge of being overrun by beetles, and no spraying was necessary there. The birds and the wasps did a more effec-tive job than any spray-gun troops could possibly do. But until the natural checks of this type do move in to halt inroads of such pests as the bark beetles, the Forest Service has the gigantic job of stopping these tiny tree-destroyers that in recent years have killed as much as six to seven times as much valuable wood as have the flames of forest fires. In recent years Region 1 has had its share of "bug control" to contend with.

V I

BEGINNING at the easterly side, the forests of Region 1 are the Custer, the Lewis and Clark, the Gallatin, the Helena, the Flathead, the Deer Lodge, the Beaverhead, the Bitterroot, the Nezperce, the Clearwater, the Lolo, the St. Joe, the Kootenai, the Kaniksu, the Coeur d'Alene, and the Colville. Some of the wildest of our wilderness areas are in these forests. Here too there are more big-game species than in most regions: grizzly and black bears, antelope in some lower parts of the forests, the elk, mule deer, white-tail deer, Shiras moose, bighorn sheep, and mountain goats. In the streams are the rainbow and cutthroat native trout, salmon of several species, grayling, Williamson's whitefish, and a number of other fishes that can supply sport and food.

The entire region includes more than 31,000,000 acres within exterior national-forest boundaries. Of this total nearly 28,000,000 acres are owned by the public. The bulk of the land administered by Region 1 staffs is in the national forests, but there are more than 3,000,000 acres in LU lands.

The data that follow pertain to Montana only (the forests of Region 1 in Idaho hold comparable values and qualities):

There are 22,359,000 acres of all classes of forest in Montana. This is about a fourth of the total area of the state. Fifty-eight per cent of this forest territory lies west of the Continental Divide and is a sixth of the total area of the state.

Montana's "commercial forest" contains 56,000,000,000 board feet of saw timber. Half of this is made up of two tree species, western larch and Douglas fir. Lodgepole, ponderosa pine, and Englemann spruce make up most of the remaining half. Seventy-six per cent of this forest area is publicly owned. About half of the area of the national forests of Region 1, 13,923,000 acres, is in this state. About three fourths of the existing saw timber is publicly owned or managed. The annual growth on trees 5 inches or more in diameter adds up to about 606,000,000 board feet.

At this rate, the present growth increment of forests in Montana represents a gain of about 38 board feet per acre per year. It is estimated that when all the land that should be growing wood is producing under good management plans, this 38 board feet per year can be raised to 85 board feet per year per acre.

Since the first sawmill began to cut lumber in the 1840s, 20,000,000,000 board feet have been cut from Montana's forests. And if the fires can be controlled, the insects and diseases checked, the best practices of forest management applied, a far greater contribution to our needs for wood and its products will be coming out of this northernmost region of the Forest Service in the Rocky Mountain west.

VI

CRADLES OF RIVERS

I

WE HAVE marked how forests are associated with mountain country. The soils, slopes, and heights of mountains supply inviting habitat for trees and all the life associated with them.

West of the 100th Meridian to the foothills of the Rockies is the empire of the grass lands. Once the foothills are reached the flats that stretch out from the bases of the mountains are more often mesquite, sagebrush, cactus, and creosote bush desert than grass country. Even high-slung intermountain valleys may be arid if surrounding mountains catch the clouds and prevent rain falling within those basins. As an example, the San Luis Valley of southern Colorado has an average of 8 inches of precipitation—little more rainfall than the driest portions of the sun-scoured deserts of Arizona and Sonora.

The fact that mountainous country usually is timber country is demonstrated in the forests of Region 1. Southward, in Region 2, the emphasis on mountains as the homelands of forests is even more pronounced. Region 2 contains most of our highest peaks. According to the latest data, the U.S. Geological Survey lists 69 mountains in continental United States which reach or exceed 14,000 feet above sea level. Colorado had boasted for years that 52 peaks of 14,000 feet elevation were within her borders. In 1956 the U.S. Geological Survey added Huron and Missouri, high points in the Collegiate Range, to the list.

All but one (Longs Peak) of these Colorado peaks are inside boundaries of national forests. Longs Peak is the dominating high point in the Rocky Mountain National Park. The Park is surrounded by the 1,085,143-acre Roosevelt National Forest on its easterly sides, and the 1,074,672-acre Arapaho National Forest on the west. So if we were to reach the top of any 14,000-foot peak in Colorado, parts of all of one or more national forests would be spread out below us.

High points in Wyoming also overlook national forests. The state's highest point, Fremont Peak, is in the Wind River mountains which stretch southward from Yellowstone National Park and form part of the Continental Divide. It has an elevation of 13,730 feet. This highest point, east of Jackson Hole, is on the boundary between the Shoshone National Forest of Region 2 and the Teton National Forest, which is in Region 4.

Eastward from Fremont Peak and the Shoshone Forest, across stretches of broken-up country, the Bighorn mountains mass high. Cloud Peak, with an elevation of 13,165 feet, is the apex of this range, which is mostly within the Bighorn National Forest. Still farther eastward, in South Dakota, are the Black Hills, practically all of which except a portion owned by the state are in the Black Hills National Forest. The thumb of granite core rock which shoved up to become Harney Peak rises to 7,240 feet above sea level. It is the highest point in this national forest, in South Dakota, and the highest spot east of the main ranges of the Rockies.

Usually the Black Hills are considered a wholly separate mountain mass, an orphan range that straggled out on the prairies and lodged there. A height of land exists in eastern Wyoming on one side of which rainfall flows into the Belle Fourche River, which follows a route north of the Black Hills to join the Missouri, or, falling on the other side of the ridge, drains to the Cheyenne River, which flows eastward on the south side of the Hills. The foundation of core rock below this divide connects the Hills with the Bighorns and the Rockies. It probably is of no particular consequence to note that this tie exists between the Hills and the mountains to the west, although it does suggest the magnitude of the stresses that cracked the earth's surface here. And it calls attention to how the Hills are linked to the Rockies.

Having referred rather glibly to Region 2's great mountains I should hasten to define my sub-amateur rating as an alpinist. Throughout the years I traveled across and around the Rockies from Montana to New Mexico, I never climbed a mountain merely to master it. There have been moments in which I felt the keen satisfaction that comes only as one concludes a reasonably demanding ascent. I have friends who have sought out and climbed all 14,000-foot peaks in Colorado, western Canada, Mexico, several in Europe, and some great peaks of the sky-ripping Andes. This is their chosen sport. It has its gripping lure, and I credit them with their achievements. My choice in outdoor sports has been fishing. But I do know you do not have to master a mountain to like it.

Except California's Mount Whitney, Washington's Mount Rainier, and Longs Peak (the first is partly and the other two are wholly within national parks), all of our peaks of 14,000 or more feet are in national forests. For good measure there are scores topping the 12,000-foot mark and hundreds that are at least 10,000 feet above sea level. It follows that among these one may find every gradation in mountain-climbing, from a gentle walk to climbs requiring the chilling antics of advanced climbers.

One may ride comfortably in an auto or a cog-road coach to the top of Pikes Peak or by auto to the top of Mount Evans; both Colorado peaks are more than 14,000 feet high. But one must feel the drag of the climb in leg muscles, the thinness of the cool air in lungs, the hammer of pulse beating rapidly because of the effort and low oxygen content of the rarefied atmosphere if one is to appreciate to the fullest what these master mountains can give. I hold that viewing mountains from an airplane cannot approach the enjoyment and understanding secured from a high overlook. Looking down from the plane you see mountains merely as rough spots on a flattened world. They deny the character of their mass and height to anyone who tries to appraise their dignity and magnificence by utilizing mechanical wings.

I have given first mention to mountains as we come to Region 2 because with the exception of the two sections of the Nebraska National Forest, where lusty growing pines have been planted, the national forests here are the mountain lands.

I I

Leaving Montana and entering Region 2, the first town south of the state boundary is Cody, Wyoming, where the headquarters of the Shoshone National Forest is located. There are nearly 2,500,000 acres in the Shoshone, including many acres that were in that very first "forest reserve" established in 1891. Two large forests were combined to form this one large unit, the old Washakie and the original Shoshone.

The east entrance to Yellowstone National Park, via Cody, traverses the Shoshone canyon. In 1919, when this

highway still was only graveled and replete with chuck-
holes, I rode with Supervisor John Lowell in his old touring-car to enter Yellowstone by Sylvan Pass. Wind and rain
shaped the Devil's Elbow, the Stone Goose, the King of
Ireland and other gnomish rock formations in this canyon
—it is a wonderland for those who delight in seeing faces
and forms in rocks. Near the upper reaches of the canyon
we stopped at Pahaska Tepee to tarry in its lingering aura.

William Frederick Cody, who began life in a farm community near Davenport, Iowa, and later did the chores on
his family's homestead in Kansas, had built Pahaska Tepee as his place of retreat after a busy life. This structure,
burdened with gimcrack log work, was a mixture of resort,
peaceful sanctuary, show place, and tourist trading-post
when we saw it not long after Colonel Cody, better known
as Buffalo Bill, had died in Denver.

There are hundreds of thousands of wild-country acres
in this forest and its neighbors. Happily they form a buffer zone around Yellowstone National Park and contain
big areas of the nearest thing we have today to western
mountain wilderness. Some of the finest wilderness is in
the southern part of the Shoshone which formerly was
the Washakie National Forest.

I I I

The headquarters of the Washakie was in the Federal
Building at Lander, Wyoming. As may be found often in
national-forest communities, there is a special western quality about this town. Lander is, for one thing, the western
terminus of the Chicago & Northwestern Railway. Beyond
the end of these rails *is* the west.

The coming of the railway to Lander underwrote a very early program of "rotation cutting" of railway ties. In the 1920s the Wyoming Tie and Timber Company was cutting approximately half of the fully mature lodgepole pines on a watershed unit of the Wind River above Dubois, Wyoming. Later the woods crews would move on to the next unit, where they would cut about half of the trees ready for harvest. This partial cut would be repeated every 40 years. It was an "80-year-rotation" management program. I encountered a very significant fact on that timber sale. About four years after a hillside was thus cut the average person would swear it never had echoed the ring of axes. Reproduction came in to fill open spaces so rapidly that the forest as a whole gave the effect of unscarred wilderness.

How better knowledge is constantly changing forest management plans to produce more wood is indicated by what has happened to this 80-year rotation on the old Washakie. Foresters have found that clear cutting produces, in the long run, more lodgepole pines of usable quality than the selective cutting. It is probable that more time must pass before a clear-cut forest will regain the qualities of wilderness.

Another change has taken place. In the 1920s Lander and its neighbor towns would have many Scandinavian tie hacks on the streets after pay days; they'd also hear them, for brawls would often break out. These men who used broad axes to square the ties (and literally did hack squared timbers out of round logs) were experts among ax-men. Today's ties are not "hacked." They are cut square in sawmills by machines operated by a different breed of men.

A mountain stream, the Middle Fork of the Popo Agie, comes out of the foothills to course through Lander. Local luminaries, for some unknown reason, pronounce this river's name "po-posh-ia" with the "o" long in both instances, and the "s" a shooshing sound somewhere between a "c" and a "z." My good friend the late Judge Joseph Fourt declared this supposed Indian name was correctly pronounced "po-po aggie."

From Lander a road beside the little river leads up into the foothills, where, past inviting picnic spots, are "The Sinks." This, a not very inviting name, is descriptive, for here the Popo Agie's Middle Fork encountered some sedimentary plates of earth crust which had been heaved up so that at one time they blocked the stream's way to the plains. A similar stream in another location might have excavated a corridor. This little river ducked under the limestone-sandstone hogback formation.

The Popo Agie is consistently a clear stream—a brawling bit of river, white with tossed water. After it ducks under at "The Sinks" it boils out from its subterranean adventuring. Such mountain streams of medium size are skeins of clear water that mountains and foothills spin into brooks and creeks. They then escape the highlands and run out to the prairies and plains. There they are braided into important rivers.

Now I invite you to join our trail party as it left Lander for the hills on July 2, 1922. Our guide and packer was Arthur Robinson, a man near in skills and spirit to the men of the fur brigades who traced through here a century earlier. Our host was Judge Fourt. He organized this expedition to the forest back country so that Forbes Parkhill and I might become acquainted with his favorite Wind River Mountains.

We swung to saddles at the Whittaker ranch where its buildings squatted in the outward corridor cut by the North Fork of the Popo Agie. The boxy canyon is a portal dug through the great, slanting, flat-faced plates of sedimentary rocks sloping like gigantic shingles toward the plains. These tipped sedimentary formations extend all along the eastern edges of the main ranges of our Rockies. You see them in Red Rocks Park west of Denver, in the Garden of the Gods at Colorado Springs, and in many unnamed but curious stone landscapes in the outer foothill belt from Montana to Mexico.

The trail we traveled out from the Whittaker ranch followed the stream for a little way, then zigzagged into switchbacks to climb across the south face of the local Bald Mountain. By late afternoon we reached our "camp" —the one-room log cabin and pole corral of the North Fork Ranger Station. The Judge said we'd have time to do a bit of angling.

Two encounters with wildlife are vivid in my memories of that spot. One is the horde of big-headed, fully matured brook trout about six inches long which existed in those high-country brooks near the cabin. They had perhaps only two months each year for feeding on terrestrial insects. Winter comes early and lingers long in the high country. Dangling any sort of artificial fly over the water would bring hungry trout leaping crazily to grab at something they thought might be food. They were stunted also by the coldness of the water, for it was only a degree or two above the temperature of the snowdrifts from which the creeks trickle.

The other recollection is of mosquitoes. Why they should "hatch out of the snowdrifts" in the Wind River Mountains as they seem to do, I have never fathomed. They were so abundant at the North Fork Ranger Station that they would practically form a layer over any exposed skin and begin to prospect with fire-tipped drills. They were big, aggressive, and insistent on taking their blood toll for your invasion of their territory.

The morning after we put in at the Middle Fork Ranger Station we sought an overlook spot. Mount Chauvenet is not to be found on most maps; it is not a tremendous height among western mountains though its apex is 12,280 feet above sea level.

Our climb to the top of Mount Chauvenet in the Wind River range on that July day was to secure a point of overlook. In the years I traveled the Rockies on foot, horseback, by buckboard, stage, truck, train, and auto, I have never found an outlook point presenting a wilder, more fiercely beautiful country than we saw that day from the top of Chauvenet.

To the north lay a cove in the mountain mass that is the western part of the Shoshone Indian Reservation. Cove is a relative term, for it is filled with ridges, canyons, lakes, and forests. Directly west of Chauvenet we looked down on Washakie Lake east of Washakie Pass, and near Mount Washakie, landmark monuments to the old chief.

Northward, past Mount Hooligan, Mount Bonneville, peaks 1, 3, 4, and 7 (all on the Continental Divide), we could see the highest Wyoming mountains, Fremont and Gannett peaks. We saw the ice cap on the Divide, the most extensive in the country. This is a little known scenic area, but savagely alluring. Here and there ice thrust off the Divide into several glaciers, the largest of these ice rivers being the one above Bull Lake. In the ice-dug basins below the east face of this range were lakes, many still frozen over on that July day.

We gazed across mountain country that is almost unchanged since Bridger, Fitzpatrick, Ashley, Carson, Bonneville, and other early adventurers before and after them came through this part of the Rockies. Within sight were many spots where battles between Indian tribes were fought. In the dim distance, north of the Wind River, we could glimpse the location of Crowheart Butte—and again we thought of this land, with its faint trails in the canyons below us, as the land of Washakie.

Washakie was chief of the Shoshones. He was brave and wise—a genuinely great man. Once when the Crow Indians raided into the Shoshone territory, Washakie and some members of his tribe took refuge on the flattopped piece of land called Crowheart Butte. The young, hot-headed Shoshones wanted to sally forth and fight. Washakie knew that battle would gain little and that it would mean death for many. He refused to sanction attack on the superior numbers of the Crow war party. The young men sneered and called him a coward. Washakie allowed this to pass— for the moment.

That night, without any announcement, he visited the Crow camp. He was back among his own band by daylight. He spread the contents of a package he carried before his warriors. In it was the heart of a Crow Indian. Washakie had entered the enemy camp during darkness, had killed one of the sleeping war party, procured gory evidence of his having been there, and returned with it to confute those who had called him a coward. That is the story of how Crowheart Butte got its name.

The Shoshones never warred with explorers or settlers. Washakie saw that it would be better policy to work with the incoming white people. So it was that when the relief column journeyed to the battlefield of the Little Bighorn, the site of "Custer's Last Stand," Washakie and his Shoshone scouts rode ahead of the troops.

I should have liked to meet Washakie. I had the privilege of meeting his youngest son, Dick, who was a lad in his early teens when he traveled with that column going to the Little Bighorn battleground. Dick Washakie was very proud of the bronze medal issued to the Shoshones in token of their help on that expedition. Whenever the council of six old men and six young men gathered in the tribal room at Fort Washakie, Dick was there with the little bronze disk and its tattered ribbon pinned to his old, black dress-up coat. Dick has joined his father, the chief, in the cemetery at Fort Washakie, where also are the remains of Sacajawea, the girl who guided Lewis and Clark. Some claim that her grave is elsewhere, but among my friends are those who remember Sacajawea living at the fort and her death and burial.

When we came in from that trip to the top of Chauvenet, and scrubbed away trail taint under a good hot shower, drums began to throb. Shoshones and Arapahos danced in Lander's streets because the morrow would be the Fourth of July. Occasionally during the night I awakened to hear drums and chanting. Early the next forenoon I boarded the stage, an automobile of World War I vintage, to travel by way of South Pass to Rock Springs. There I would catch a train to Laramie. Our way led through Atlantic City and South Pass City, Wyoming.

Cities? Perhaps someone so named them hoping that eventually they might merit the rating. Wyoming's Atlantic City, which can offer several board walks, in 1954 boasted of a population of 50 souls and South Pass City is almost as large with 33 residents.

You must watch along the road for a marker that will locate South Pass. This part of the Continental Divide is not a sharp ridgepole but a wide prairie. Look closely and you may see here ruts made by many covered wagons that traveled the Overland Trail.

The first white men to cross here were Astorians, led by

Robert Stuart, on October 21, 1812. Captain B. L. E. Bonneville and his party traversed this wide-flung prairie in 1832. On July 1, 1836, the Reverend Marcus Whitman chose this route to demonstrate that a wheeled vehicle could cross the Divide and reach the West Coast. His wife, Narcissa, and one Eliza Hart were the first white women to travel this route.

This is a key spot on the old Oregon trail, the California Trail, the Mormon Trail, and the Overland Stage system, and it is on the original route of the east-and-west Pony Express. All crossed here at South Pass. Westward are Dry Sandy, Little Sandy, and Big Sandy stage stations, famous stops of the Overland. Eastward are the sites of Fort Stambaugh, the "Three Crossings" of the Sweetwater, Devil's Gate, and Independence Rock.

Lonesome and deserted as South Pass may now be, it once was a very important spot on a most important highway.

Some of the buildings still standing or tottering are believed to be those built when these Cities of the Pass were halting places along those trails of yesterday. In 1922 some structures were refurbished and some were reasonably new, for there had been a "revival" a few years earlier when a mining boom swept this area. The tungsten shortage of World War I sparked this moment of rejuvenation. A recent report on the status of the "Cities" lists as still in business one of those modest but often delightful hotels left in pleasant eddies and backwaters as modern travel lines have siphoned away most of the local enterprises and population. Are these "ghost towns"? Not so long as you can find food and lodging there.

I V

WERE this a travelogue, we should continue on the route, as I did in 1922, by rail to Laramie, by car through Centennial, Wyoming, the site of a faded mining boom, and on to encounter six-foot snowdrifts still blocking the road a half mile from the Brooklyn Ranger Station in the Medicine Bow National Forest. We'd shelter in the station, catch fat trout out of ice-fringed Lake Marie below the up-sweeping cliffs of the Snowy Range, then travel horseback across this spur of the Rockies to the Ames Ranger Station where the streams flow into the North Platte. From there we'd thread along trails to the tie camp at Fox Park and then return by auto to Laramie.

We'd visit the Bighorn National Forest and the Seven Brothers lakes, each stocked with a different kind of trout. We'd see Misty Moon Pass. We would camp at the Bighorn forest's Lake Solitude, a spot of wilderness sanctuary where during the early 1950s only stubborn insistence by the nation's conservationists prevented a major desecration of this gem-like lake by a Bureau of Reclamation dam.

But since this is not intended to be an orthodox guidebook, I ask you to bypass these intermediate areas and seek certain high places in Colorado.

V

IN MY first weeks with the U.S. Forest Service, one of my good forester friends, Wallace Hutchinson, made a remark about Region 2's San Isabel National Forest which sounded slightly contemptuous. "Hutch," who had been one of Pinchot's young foresters, spent quite a few years in the Philippines. There trees do grow like weeds and against this background he had reason to call the San Isabel a "brush forest." It is true that trees growing on slopes of the Rocky Mountains from Wyoming to Mexico add less wood to their trunk and limbs than do those in most of the other regions. But calling the national forests of these middle and southern Rockies "brush forests" is a relative statement.

There are great trees with good sawlogs in their stems in all Region 2 forests; there are millions of acres bearing conifers which are stately and contain billions of board feet of lumber. But more important than these wood values is the protection they give to critical slopes of many watersheds. Region 2 is the cradle of important rivers.

The San Isabel is first of all a watershed forest. No great rivers are born within its boundaries. But from its canyons rush many little streams. Bare hillsides would soon be stripped to skeleton rocks if timber and shrubs were removed, and the little streams would be flooding after each rain and be dry washes at other times.

The San Isabel is one of my favorite national forests. It lies in three divisions. The Sierra Mojada of Spanish explorers, today's Wet Mountains, rise on the horizon west of Pueblo, Colorado. The core-rock bones of this portion of the forest are more than a billion years old; they are among the oldest rocks you may find in any western mountains. Though the rock itself is that old, it was thrust from the center of the planet along with other parts of the Rockies a mere 60,000,000 years or so ago—a fairly recent event.

The Wet Mountains have a considerable resemblance to the time-smoothed eastern mountains. There is enough precipitation on their eastern slopes to produce fairly abundant plant growth, which enhances that resemblance. And, like eastern mountain country, these mountains are replete with history, legend, and folklore.

The Second Mace is a high valley where robbers of the Pueblos-Taos stage made headquarters. The highest peak, Greenhorn Mountain, or in Spanish, Querno Verde, which more exactly is "Green Horn," was named for a Comanche chief killed near its east base in 1778. The Spanish troops in this battle were under orders from Juan Batista de Anza, who had become colonial governor at Santa Fe after choosing the site some time earlier of the presidio that became San Francisco.

Near the northerly end of this division, adjacent to Hardscrabble Creek, is the location of the first of the several frontier trading-posts built and in time abandoned by the Bent brothers. The last, longest used, and most famous of their establishments was Bent's Fort on the Arkansas River. There the Santa Fe trail struck southwest toward the landmark Spanish Peaks and Raton Pass.

A second and most southerly division of the forest contains these Spanish Peaks. They are volcanic mountains, cone shaped, and called by the Ute Indians, Wa-ha-toy-ah, which becomes less lyrical in its literal translation: "Squaw's Breasts." The third division of the San Isabel contains Colorado's portion of the Sangre de Cristo mountains.

Al Hamel, at that time Supervisor of this forest, and I had traveled out of the Hardscrabble Canyon one late afternoon to face westward across the mighty sweep of the Wet Mountain Valley. We had passed the nearly abandoned mining-camp named Querida and were on the straight stretch of graveled road east of the ghost town of Silver Cliff—the site of the nigh legendary Bassick Mine and locale of Helen Hunt Jackson's book, *Nell's Silver Mine.*

Al stopped the old touring-car and said: "Let's look for a few minutes."

Against the western sky the Cristos at sundown stood sharp-edged as if cut from tin. Shafts of sunlight lanced across V-cut saddles between the peaks. The sky became shimmering blue. A few first lights in ranch houses began to twinkle in the vastness of shadows on the west side of the valley.

"How many peaks over ten thousand can be seen from this spot?" asked Al. "There's Humboldt, Kit Carson, the Crestones all above fourteen thousand elevation. You count those peaks over ten thousand feet and I will too."

Al's tally was 54 or 55 peaks estimated over 10,000 elevation, and I had two or three less than his count. A couple of peaks that might be above or below that elevation wouldn't make much difference in the Cristos.

The Sangre de Cristos march in rhythmic single file from Salida, Colorado, near the spot where Poncha Pass lies between the Cristos and the Continental Divide, to a point over a hundred miles southward near Taos, New Mexico. Only in one or two spots does this range have a thickness at its base of more than six to ten miles. It is a single-line chain of mountains.

I like the Cristos for their sharp, incisive forms, their positive rhythm and lack of confusion. They also intrigue me with history that is laced all over their slopes.

Spanish explorers from Santa Fe crossed these mountains by a whole series of passes. Among these were La Veta Pass, now used by U.S. Highway 160, and, in succession northward, Sangre de Cristo Pass, Pass Creek, Mosca, Medano, and Music passes. None boasts a modern road except La Veta. Zebulon Pike and his party

deadly than fire may be the killing of great
s by tiny insects. The dead trees are Englemann
e, killed by legions of spruce-bark beetles.

At Fraser, Colorado, at one of Region 2's experiment stations, alternate clear-cut strips through a forest of spruce and fir are tested as a means for trapping more snow and delivering more water into the Colorado River's priceless flow.

The grazing of domestic livestock is th practical method of utilizing the crops c age that grow in the national forest.

ion 4, noted for its quantity and ety of wildlife, also contains tacular scenic features, such as Falls on the Snake River in the ghee National Forest.

d beauty of rugged mountains he Sawtooth National Forest in ho is mirrored in Redfish Lake.

Winter is crisis time for the wildlife. These mule deer were photographed in the Teton National Forest in western Wyoming.

Pack trains carry those seeking the most remote places into Region 4's Idaho Wilderness.

difference between limited grazing and
kinned earth of an over-grazed area is
n dramatically in this picture of grass-
in the Tonto National Forest of Arizona.

Range grasses, livestock, watershed, and soil
are all in good condition when grazing is kept
within proper limits. These sleek Hereford
cattle thrive on the Jornada Experimental
Range in New Mexico.

The roots of the low shrubs, weeds, and grasses protect the surface of this "island" in the middle of a flood-cut arroyo. Vertical walls have prevented livestock from grazing the top of the island.

In areas of tender soils and tumultuous c[loud]bursts, rain water may sweep in sheets a[cross] valley lands, cutting little gullies that [con]tribute silt to the destructive floods.

gers scaling logs at log decks
r the storage pond of the Boise-
ette Lumber Mill at Cascade,
ho.

n the mountainsides and valleys
egion 1, the straight-grained
gs are gathered into the stor-
ond beside the mill of the J.
Lumber Company at Libby,
ana.

The cry of "Fire!" sends the clou[d] parachutes of the Smoke Jumpe[rs] billowing over the Salmon Natio[nal] Forest in Idaho.

Short-wave radio, with its high [mo]bility, aids the modern fire-figh[ter]

crossed Medano Pass on foot on Wednesday, January 28, 1807. The stage road to old Fort Massachusetts crossed Mosca Pass in the days when Kit Carson was associated with that post. Earlier, Carson's fur brigades had traveled all these corridors through the Cristos as they sought peltry farther north. And Antoine Roubideau, an early fur trader, led the first wagon train from the plains to western Colorado through the defile of Mosca Pass.

From an old log cabin on this Mosca Pass in October 1920 I sallied out with ranger Karl Gilbert on my first big game hunt. The evening before the last day of the open season found us with no venison in camp. Karl thought we might get at least one buck if we hunted early at timberline on California Hill, a long, level-top ridge south of the pass. Loaded with improvised back-packs slung in blankets, we labored up the north face of California Hill in time to watch sundown light the skies above the Continental Divide far to the west across the San Luis Valley.

We shivered through the timberline night beside a great fire of old fir stumps. We downed black scalding coffee before first graying of the morning while Karl blocked out where and how we would hunt. I had my first and practically only case of buck fever that day. A shadowy deer shape moved through the edge of the woods, but I saw no horns. There *were* no antlers. But until I could see in quickening light that it was so, I watched that doe and shook so I'd surely have missed any shot if it had been a buck. We tallied no venison that season.

This last and luckless day of the deer season was born cloudless. As the sunshine began to carry a touch of warmth, I quit the hunting, found a spot on the east side of a ledge, and watched the big show of the new day's arrival.

A climax of beauty came just before the first thin slice of the sun showed above plains far out toward Kansas. The atmosphere seemed to take on a pronounced opalescence. All around me was thin mountain air, but it was so full of color it seemed almost tangible. Eastward, toward the Great Plains, there was a tinted land brushed with brown and gold undertones, but overlaid with the luster of pearls. Westward—because the mountains were between it and the sunrise—the great 80-mile sweep of the San Luis Valley was a pool of shadow. The shadow began to evaporate from its western edge as the sun began to climb.

There was that moment of mystery and beauty, and then the sun got free of the horizon. The first light rays that had splashed the higher peaks to the north, and Sierra Blanca's top to the south, flowed down their sides and spread along California Hill. The sun's warmth felt good as I saw the details of the lands below begin to emerge from shadow. Shortly all features were sharp, bright, and clear.

From heights such as this ridge you can see the veins of the earth's hydrological cycle—the little creeks that gather into larger creeks to become small rivers and finally the majestic flow lines by which life-bearing water that has gone through the capillaries of the clouds returns to the heart of the ocean. Passing over a watershed in a plane you may glance toward the ground and find interest for a moment in the way the small channels join much like the bare twigs of trees to become the principal limbs and then the river's trunk. Before you can puzzle out all the pattern you are above another basin. At the top of a mountain you trace the routes of flow and have time to interpret what you see.

On the east side of California Hill lies the basin of the Huerfano River. It joins the Arkansas River miles across the plains, far to the northeast. Huerfano drainage is to the Gulf of Mexico by way of the Mississippi. West of the ridge the mountain-rimmed San Luis Valley once held a big lake. It had drained, according to one interpretation by geologists, by way of Mosca or an adjacent pass to an ancient river antedating the Arkansas. But eventually waters had seeped and sluiced and sliced through fractures in rock dikes at the south end of this basin. The bowl of the San Luis Valley gathers the primary waters to form the Rio Grande del Norte, which dug a canyon where the seep had first trickled southward from the valley.

Near the center of Colorado, close to famous Leadville, the Rocky Mountains pile up their highest elevations in Mount Elbert and Mount Massive. Here is a tumult of mountains, canyons, gulches, and ridges. Streams finding their way to less tumbled terrain must twist and turn in their course. In the high gulches and arctic tundra in and near this apex of the main mountains are the headwaters of five important rivers.

First is the Colorado, into which all the waters falling west of the Continental Divide in Region 2 finally gather. The North Platte runs straight north out of central Colorado into Wyoming, turns east, then southeast to flow by the town of North Platte in Nebraska. The South Platte runs south in the basin eastward of Leadville, then turns east, then north, then east to reach the plains, then flows northeast through Denver and toward its junction with the North Platte in Nebraska. The Arkansas begins so close to the Colorado and the South Platte (where the highest rills start running) that a snowdrift on a ridge could melt into one drainage on one side to reach the Pacific Ocean, and on the other side of the ridgepole flow to the Gulf of Mexico. Finally the mountain basin of El Rio Grande del Norte can be identified by looking south-

ward from many of the mountain tops in this highest part
of the Divide.

Approximately three fourths of all land within the
United States 10,000 feet or more above sea level is in
Colorado. There are about 20,000,000 acres of water-pro-
ducing lands in this state. Trapped by higher peaks and
ridges, made to spill their moisture loads, the clouds drop
rain and snow mostly on the areas 7,500 feet or more
above sea level. From these lands, which are predominantly within national forests, there is an average yearly
outflow of 16,600,000 acre feet.

About a third of this flow is "used" within Colorado
—by municipalities, manufacturers, and irrigation farmers. The other two thirds flows beyond the state's borders
to service communities in other places—in some cases
fields and cities a thousand or more miles away.

If we were to put so modest a value as $5 per acre foot
on this water that is mostly gathered within the national
forests, the 16,600,000 acre feet would be worth $80,-
000,000 annually. By the time an acre foot of the Colorado river water arrives at acres growing citrus or vegetable
crops in California, it may have a value of $100. Actually,
there can be no fixed dollar measure for what we must
have to sustain life. In the west water from the forest
basins underwrites life.

Perhaps the stake that many people have in Region 2's
national forests can be indicated by such facts as these.
Approximately 72 per cent of the flow of the Colorado
River, that is, the water on which rests the existence of
many communities of the southwest, is gathered and delivered out of the national forests in Colorado. More than
half of the flow in the Rio Grande is from the forests of
southern Colorado. And both the Arkansas and Platte
drainages, embracing practically all of those lands on the

east side of the Continental Divide from South Pass in Wyoming to that basin of the Huerfano I saw from California Hill, *get almost their total flow* from streams born in our national forests in Colorado and southern Wyoming.

Region 2 of the U.S. Forest Service contains the cradles in which are born five of the important rivers of the west.

The forests of Region 2 must be regarded as of primary importance in protecting watershed values. At the same time their other contributions to community well being must not be slighted.

In recent years forests of Region 2 have had annual timber sales that amounted to 217,964,000 board feet of lumber. For this timber as it stood, unharvested on the stump, operators paid $1,160,048.

The tourist business of the west depends in no small measure on the existence of these great, inviting public forests. In Colorado alone the estimated number of visitors from other states in 1956 (which was a fairly representative year) totaled 3,583,000 people. They spent an estimated $208,600,000 in that one season. This does not include the recreational use of the forests made by Colorado residents; a summary of that probably would more than double both estimates. And it probably would be conservative to estimate that the forests in Wyoming and the Black Hills serve recreational uses not less than half the magnitude—in numbers of visitors and amounts spent by recreationists—that was tallied in Colorado.

Also, privately owned livestock utilizes forage grown on national-forest lands. In Region 2 in 1956 there were 245,000 head of cattle; 767,000 head of sheep and goats grazed on these forests for a limited few but important weeks in terms of livestock production. The $660,272 the owners paid for this privilege is only a fraction of the value this use represented to owners of the stock.

We still are in Region 2 at the top of Chama Peak in the Rio Grande National Forest. From here you look to the south, into Region 3. There below us are northern acres of the Carson National Forest. The Jicarilla Apache reservation adjoins the northern portion of the Carson. In and near Region 3's forests are little placitas that have adobe-walled homes in which people of Spanish ancestry have lived since the late sixteenth century. Pueblo tribesmen have lived in other adobe dwellings for a much longer span of time. Farther south in Region 3 is where the Cochise culture was located. The Cochise were a people who inhabited this part of our land when there were hardwood forests growing where deserts are now. Fragments of partially burned walnut wood have been found in remains of the Cochise people's campfires that flickered, smouldered, and died 10,000 years ago.

There is a tremendous array of national-forest features and values in Region 2 which we have not touched. But we must move on into the part of the nation that the writer Mary Austin labeled "The Land of Little Rain," and archaeologist Adolph Francis Alphonse Bandelier nearly seventy years ago described as the homeland of "The Delight Makers."

This area, which includes all of New Mexico and Arizona, is Region 3 of the U.S. Forest Service.

VII
LAND OF LITTLE RAIN

I

THE earth has two "desert belts." Generally these lie between 20 and 40 degrees longitude, north and south of the equator. This belt contains Africa's Sahara, the Gibson, Great Victoria, and Simpson deserts of Australia, the Empty Quarter of Saudi Arabia, and much of New Mexico and Arizona, which are the whole of Region 3.

A simplified explanation of why deserts exist between these latitudes would be somewhat as follows. Cloud masses that float across the lands are mostly the evaporated moisture from the seven seas. These clouds wallow along in streams of winds which follow fairly definite routes across the land masses. In addition to every cloud you see there are tons and tons of additional water in the sky as vapor. A large part of the moisture thus transported has evaporated from the surfaces of the seas adjacent to the equator and in the United States is carried in a curving, northeasterly direction.

Other air movements moving southeasterly bring cold fronts down from polar regions. When two of these air masses of different temperatures butt into each other, the heavier cold air slides as a wedge under the moist, warmer air, the latter rises, clouds thicken and chill, tiny crystals form as embryonic snowflakes, increase in size, and fall to the earth as snow, sleet, and hail—or, melting on the way down, become rain.

[183]

The desert belt is that in-between zone across which moisture-carrying winds travel *before* the moist warm air meets a mass of cold polar air and part of the moisture load is dropped.

About 10,000 years ago parts of today's Region 3 may have resembled the Ozark mountain country. The most recent glaciers then lay over the midland plains and cold air that triggered rain over these lands was abundant. Fresh-water lakes of size spread out for miles where shrinking remnant lakes or dry lake beds now lie. Prehistoric Lake Bonneville, which was much larger than today's Great Salt Lake, filled a great intermountain basin with fresh water, and its overflow reached the western ocean by way of the Columbia. A lake preceding today's Pyramid Lake in northern Nevada also held fresh water, as did a basin in eastern New Mexico.

A hundred centuries ago hardwood trees grew in the southwest. Archaeologists have found partially burned pieces of walnut wood which once had smoldered in a fire lit by a very early inhabitant of southern Arizona and New Mexico—a person of a race long vanished, the ancient Cochise culture.

The ice fields retreated, air currents changed directions, drought fastened on the southwest, and the Cochise people disappeared. Through gradual changes the desert plant life covered the soils formed and stabilized during prior climatic conditions.

The lower country throughout Region 3 being desert, the association of forests with mountains is sharply demonstrated here. The heavy mists, fogs, and clouds that do travel across these lands are caught on the mountains and made to yield part of their moisture load before they climb the ramparts and sail across more desert to encounter another mountain range and again pay a tribute of rain or snow to the heights. Long-time records of the U.S. Weather Bureau reveal the pattern of dryness in the low country and more abundant rain in the high country.

At Yuma, Arizona (elevation 142 feet above sea level), the average annual precipitation is 3.39 inches; at Gila Bend, 118 miles east of Yuma and 737 feet above sea level, the precipitation is 5.51. To the east at Prescott, which is in the national forest of that name (elevation 5,354 feet), there is an annual precipitation of 15.98 inches; at Flagstaff (elevation approximately 7,000), the precipitation averages 18.47 inches. This pattern also holds in New Mexico. The southwest's mountains are almost the only areas in Region 3 where enough rain falls for trees of size and substance to grow.

In the two states of Region 3 are many more acres of desert than of timber-draped mountains. I would not wish any remark of mine to impair your enjoyment of the desert. It can fasten a taloned grip on those who are caught in its allures.

Look coldly at the desert before it has made you one of its devotees and you probably will see how harsh, scrawny, and cruel it appears. Then linger, and suddenly the gray, hostile land drapes its stoney features with pulsing color and a shimmer of mystery. Across baked flats you see a mirage where a false lake is edged by trees that are distorted images of only hip-high brush. At eventide the sky blazes with fire, and the Joshua trees or the distorted pillars of saguaro cactus are silhouetted against that fire. Then you'll see the stars so close at midnight a tall man on stilts might touch them. At dawn daylight comes pouring across the desert like a cataract at flood time and you are stunned by vastness, the wonder of infinite sky and measureless distance. Those who are caught in its spell demand their daily dosage of desert or they deny they are "living."

These lowlands of the southwest contain only a small part of the national-forest acreage. But these flatter lands, where cactus, sagebrush, creosote bush, and the yuccas scrabble out a fair existence, supply a particular quality to the southwest's landscapes. They are the foreground as you approach the mountains.

In the units of Regions 1 and 2—with the exception of that wide sag in the Continental Divide between South Pass and Colorado's north boundary—there is fairly continuous timbered country if you travel in the highlands from north to south.

In Region 3 there are a few places where national forests have contiguous boundaries. Generally you must cross miles of dry, flat country to get from one mountain range and its forest to another range and its timber patches.

Were they located in mountain country of Region 1 or Region 2, many of the mountain masses in Region 3 would not seem impressive. They would be merely outshooting auxiliary ranges. Surrounded as they are by the desert flatlands, often rising abruptly from extensive levels, Region 3's mountains achieve the quality of emphatic natural accent points. It is impossible to divorce them from their foreground of desert; the desert setting is a part of them. And the green timber you find in these forests seems more verdant, because to reach it you cross stretches of land where greens often are mostly a tint in a vastness that is mostly shades of gray and dun.

This desert country contains a certain sensory impact that I always recall as a part of the southwestern deserts. It is as sure to flip into my recollections as the whippoorwill song of the forests of the northeastern states, the placid twilight-swathed waters typical of the lake states, and the tremendous blanket of lodgepole pines spread on Montana mountains in my recollections of that region. My first flick of memory when I think of Region 3 is not auditory or visual, but olfactory. That country smells— pungently!

11

USUALLY as we start a tour to New Mexico and Arizona we drive southward from Denver on U.S. Highway 85. Along the 200 miles to Trinidad, Colorado, the road swings across gently arched billows of prairie that spread eastward from foothills of the Rockies. At Denver the native plant association is mostly that of the western Great Plains. Before the day ends this has been left behind.

A blending zone lies between one well-defined association of land forms and living things and another such zone. In this intermediate belt two types intermingle. You see only occasional plant groupings representative of the type into which you are traveling. Suddenly the vegetation and often the land forms are different. You know you have left one type-zone and are in another.

The fringe of growth where the mountains splay out into the flat lands presents a combination of vegetation fairly constant throughout Region 3. It is a plant community marked by piñon pines, Gambel's dwarf oak, and the cholla cactus.

An unusual isolated grove of piñon pines is located a short distance northwest of Fort Collins, Colorado, very near the Wyoming line. Scrub-oak thickets typical of New

Mexico spread over foothill slopes in certain near-by canyons and basins west of Denver. Cactus species other than the cholla thrive on dry spots all along the foothills from Mexico to Montana. Perhaps it is the cholla, with the candelabra branchings, more than the oak or pine that marks the main association of desert foothill brushlands in Region 3.

About a dozen miles north of Pueblo, Colorado, on U.S. 85, there is a cluster of buildings which bears the name of Piñon. Passing the village, you glance aside to see cholla growing on the dry rises of little hills. This has served us as a marker. From here on we know there will be more and more of things typical of the desert.

It is here, if you know what you may be testing the breeze for, that you may detect that first, faint whiff of the pungent smell I identify with Region 3. But it is only a fleeting aroma and soon left behind.

After traversing metropolitan Pueblo the desert scent washes back to you if you pause at the Huerfano River to secure a better look at the Huerfano Butte. The Butte is one of several small volcanic plugs in this locality standing raggedly beside the river a few hundred yards south of the highway. The blurps of lava tossed up by volcanic forces to make this landmark of the "Orphan Butte," supplied names for the river Huerfano, and Colorado's Huerfano county.

The desert becomes more dominant as the highway skirts the easterly base of the Wa-ha-toy-ah, reaches Trinidad, Colorado's City of the Trinity, and there begins to follow the general route of the "Military Branch" of the Santa Fe Trail. This trail, the modern U.S. 85, crosses into New Mexico by way of Raton Pass in a route followed by many through the years and centuries.

III

ON THE evening of March 7, 1862, Companies "A" and "B" of the Colorado Volunteers rendezvoused at the northern foot of this pass, crossed it, and moved to meet the Confederate army at Pigeon's ranch, which was located between today's New Mexico towns of Las Vegas and Santa Fe. There this small army, composed mostly of amateur soldiers, shattered the military expedition from the southern states which had hoped to bind into the Confederacy all the gold-producing states of our west, from Colorado to California.

In 1864 Uncle Dick Wooton built his famous road house on the north side of Raton Pass, roughed out a wagon road somewhat better than the one that had been there, established a toll gate, and charged for crossing the pass. Here also is the location of the Goodnight-Loving cattle trail—the farthest west bend of cattle trails out of Texas which laced out to all points west and north. The Atcheson, Topeka and Santa Fe crosses this high point enroute to the Pacific Coast.

In 1926 archaeologists first found stone javelin points with grooves on either side at Folsom, New Mexico, a bit east of Raton Pass. Discovered here beside ancient campfire sites and with the bones of an ancient species of bison, the points were found at other locations in association with bones of prehistoric camels and mammoths. Finding this camping-place of the "Folsom Man" near Raton Pass pushed back the estimate of how long human beings have occupied this continent to 25,000 B.C.

U.S. 85 swoops down from the pass, traverses the town of Raton, joins with U.S. 64, and 15 miles farther along the two highways take different routes toward the Rio Grande valley—U.S. 64 via Taos, U.S. 85 via Glorietta Pass. Any mountain range to the west or south of this junction which displays larger patches of timber is likely to be within the national forests of Region 3.

As the lilac tones fade or deepen on mountains seen across autumn-browned desert, or the rocky peaks seem to advance or retreat in a mirage, so the aroma of Region 3 is never quite the same in whichever hour or area you may encounter it. On a cool evening when fires are lit in the *forgones* of adobe houses in Española, New Mexico, the perfume in the dusk is predominantly the tang of piñon-pine smoke. There also, and at Mesilla, only a little distance up the Rio Grande from El Paso, there are mills that grind the fiery *chili rojo*. When these centers of production for that fierce red pepper powder that puts the bite in *chili con carne* are processing the year's crop, there could be the hint of oil of capsicum in the air. At any place you might sniff, wonder, walk down wind, and come to someone's goat corral!

But I believe that the constant body of this odor which for me so typifies Region 3's environs is the powdery, alkaline dust that hangs in the desert air.

IV

In Region 3, as in other regions, the geological history is closely interlocked with our forests of today. Earlier I suggested that most mountain soils have structures particularly suitable for the trees growing on them. At least two facts about the soils supporting the national forests of the west (well illustrated by forests in Region 3) should be stressed. The dust that gets in your nostrils in Region 3, and pricks rather than tickles, can be associated with one or both of these facts.

The first general condition is that in national forests the timber is almost wholly found growing on critical soil.

Generally the soil on the slopes of western mountains is thin, pulverized mineral stuff, a thin skin over solid rock. Much of it has been formed from disintegrated rock; other parts are decayed roots, stems, twigs, and foliage added to the mineral as many hard struggling plants gave their remains back to the earth. In many places the soil that does exist as the thin covering over hard rock is protected and held in place by the tree and shrub growth that it supports. If this protection is dissipated, the soil sloughs away, becomes silt and then dust, and the mountain sides erode to basic rock.

The second critical factor in forest-soil management throughout most of the west is steepness of slope. Often the pitch of a mountainside is far more abrupt than the stabilized slope engineers call the "angle of repose." That "repose" angle is the angle at which loose earth would stop sliding and the slope become stable.

Just below Beyer's Canyon in Grand County, Colorado, is an earthy, rock-flecked ridge that rises more than a thousand feet above the Colorado River. The entire face of that mountain is held in place by the roots of Douglas firs. It is so steep that in climbing across this slope one must follow one of the many little trails cut by the hoofs of deer that frequent the ridge. Without the binding roots of the firs that slope would be continually sloughing into the river.

Thousands of similar slopes in the west would slide and slip except for the roots laced through their soil. There are places where the mat of grasses and lesser shrubs holds the soil on a mountain side, but the best "nails" to hold a mountain's face in place are the deep driven roots of the larger woody plants.

Still another aspect of this critical problem of maintaining mats of vegetation on our national-forest uplands is the fact that some soil is "super-tender." If the protective growth were removed, this type of soil would be subject to headlong erosion.

More than a few excessively "tender" soils are located in Region 3. Many of them were laid in their present forms in the period when hardwood forests grew in parts of the southwest and cooled clouds released abundant rain. As the swing toward today's climate began, entirely different plants than those that had been growing there began to appear on the hill sides. These newcomers, which could live in a drier climate, found slopes contained rotting roots, surface litter from trees, weedy forbs and grasses, and the soil surface well blanketed with organic sponge that gradually blended into the soil.

Then came the big dry spell. Tree rings read by dendrochronologists tell of the whole earth having a dryer, milder climate. But before many soils in the southwest became so dry that they would blow into the air, that soil was nailed down by trees, shrubs, weeds, and grasses.

Over many centuries this protective blanket of plants has continued to guard the surfaces from excessive erosion. But tear that skin away even a little and disaster creeps over the land—destructive erosion begins. There are soils of the southwest so "tender" that if they are exposed to today's climatic forces *they never can be brought to stability again.* Our current climate simply cannot provide moisture to produce vegetation of the type that *did* stabilize these soils and protected them as precipitation dwindled and the once green land became our desert.

That brings us to at least one reason for the existence of the powdery dust so often encountered even in still air in Region 3. Some of the most destructive overgrazing and ensuing headlong excessive erosion by both wind and precipitation which we can find in North America is located in and near the national forests of Region 3.

Grazing, as in all national-forest regions, is a permitted use in Region 3. Flocks and herds began grazing there long ago. Over-use by grazing domestic stock on national forests and adjacent public lands in New Mexico and Arizona, and the extreme excessive erosion it has caused, is one of the ugliest instances of misuse of our federal lands to be found anywhere in the nation. This havoc is not the result of bad administration during recent years; it is a catastrophe of land abuse over many decades.

V

Before the coming of the Spanish explorers to what now is Region 3 the largest domestic animals of the pueblo Indians were captive turkeys. The bulk of the meat these people ate was procured by hunting deer, antelope, bison, bighorn sheep, and elk. As the Indians hunted this "wild livestock" they drove the herds to new range or dispersed them. Predators also moved the herds around. Game shifted range with changing seasons. Because of these shifts of the herds no range was so beaten down that it could not readily recover to produce a full crop of forage next season.

Then came men bearing arms and crosses, driving their imported domestic animals before them, to settle in 1598 at what now is the location of the San Juan pueblo, on the

Rio Grande. This pueblo Indian village still stands a few miles up river from the town of Española, New Mexico. Orñate's band of 400 soldiers and settlers did not have enough sheep, goats, and cattle to cause an adverse impact on the native forage. Generally the stock was kept on fields close to the settlement along fertile river bottoms. Through two and a half centuries Spanish colonial settlements in Arizona and New Mexico grew livestock mostly to supply the needs of the local communities.

The shift of these states from Mexican to United States territory and the opening of wagon train and railroad outlets to far away markets gave an impetus to the production of livestock for export and brought the grazer who gambled in livestock and ravaged the range. As late as 1849 a traveler who stopped for a time near Santa Fe wrote of how he crossed Galisteo creek on a plank thrown from bank to bank. This is the stream which runs west out of the hills at the foot of the La Bajada grade.

Today it is nearly an eighth of a mile from one bank of that stream to the other. Most of the year the stream bed is sunbaked sand. When the stream does flow it usually is in flood. Here we face the end product of what happens when the stabilizing ground cover, including trees, has been torn away in a semi-desert watershed.

Mostly this desertization of many basin areas in Arizona and New Mexico has resulted from overgrazing by domestic stock, and perhaps more by sheep than by cattle. The increase in livestock to destructive levels is indicated by the gain from 14,000, the number of cattle in New Mexico in 1870, to 210,000 in 1900. In the same period sheep increased from 435,000 head to 1,517,000.

First the great semi-arid valleys had the native grasses and similar forage beaten out by the grazing of so many head of domestic animals. Today when you see sage-

brush, rabbit brush, creosote bush, and their associates on
the fairly level lands between mountain ranges, you probably see a range that once was verdant with grasses "high
as a stirrup on a tall horse." Because it was cropped off
by livestock, the annual replenishment of grassy litter to
the topsoil became negligible. The protection this gave
to the more valuable fibrous-rooted grasses was lost. The
sun baked the topsoil, shallow roots were destroyed, and
only deep-rooted plants such as greasewood and sagebrush survived. Many grass ranges became brushlands with
a poor class of browse the main forage grown.

As the lower country went through successive stages of
destruction, livestock operators turned to the mountains—
the national-forest country. There they could expect more
rain, more annual growth in grasses, wildflowers, and forbs.

The collapse of markets after World War I was a major
factor in a later overloading of forest ranges. Western
stockgrowers had been called on to produce more and
more meat, leather, and wool. Suddenly the needs dimin-
ished as war ended and men who had been fighting returned to their farms in other countries and began to supply local needs. Cattle and sheep stacked up on western
ranges. Forest-grazing restrictions were eased; cattle and
sheep were "carried over" into the next season with hopes
that the markets would improve.

It was in the 1920s that livestock on the forests seriously
overtopped the carrying capacity of the ranges; it was in
those years that the pastures of the mountain forests got
such a beating that forage growth in some areas never recovered totally. This is true in spite of later considerable
reduction in livestock numbers allowed on the forests.

In 1921 permits were issued for grazing 2,050,715 cattle
and 7,412,412 sheep on all the national forests, with almost all of this livestock on western lands. Thirty years

later the Forest Service reported 1,153,246 cattle and
3,321,993 sheep on the forests. Those who know the conditions that exist in some considerable areas believe there
still is need for considerable reductions in permitted stock
in a number of forest areas.

Some of the western livestock people have made a great
issue of the Forest Service's reduction in stock permitted on
the forests. This small group has fought bitterly to hamper
the plans of the Forest Service to rescue the grasslands from
further destruction and more adequately protect other
values.

In 1946–7 this group had entrenched its leaders as higher
officials of livestock organizations and launched a campaign that came to be known as "The Great Land Grab."
They prepared legislation that proposed giving them an ex-
clusive privilege of purchasing lands within their grazing
allotments. The price of the land was to be determined on
the basis of grazing values only. A 15-year period was to
be allowed in which a potential purchaser might make up
his mind to buy his allotment, a 30-year "pay-out" period
was to follow, a down payment might be as little as 10
per cent of the total, and unpaid balances would bear interest at 1.5 per cent.

With some of the lands involved having grazing values
reckoned as low as 9¢ per acre and none higher than approximately $3 per acre, a rancher could make a down pay-
ment of 1¢ to 30¢ per acre and get title to his forest grazing
allotment. That allotment might include some tens of
thousands of acres, parts of it supporting highly valuable
timber, or it could be mineral land. But all of it could be
critical land in relation to watershed functions. The effect
on the forests would have been to shatter their homogene-
ity, lace strips of private property all through them, and
make their management and administration a nightmare.

After they were whipped in this first attempt—because the citizen-owners of the national forests became aware of what was afoot and swamped Congress with protests—this small group of acquisitive stockmen tried two later drives to get control or priority position in grazing uses of the forests. They were whipped even more soundly in these later attempts to wreck the national-forest system for their personal benefit.

About the time of the third organized push for "stockman" legislation in the Eighty-fourth Congress, a proposal appeared for modification of the Salt River watershed in Arizona. The scheme was to take most of that basin out of forest-type culture or management and convert it to predominantly grass land, ostensibly to direct more rainfall and snowmelt into irrigation reservoirs.

The Salt River Valley irrigation project dates back to 1903: it was the first irrigation project in the southwest. Water stored back of the Roosevelt Dam and in other reservoirs of the system was first used to produce field crops requiring only two to three acre feet of water per growing-season. Later garden truck and fruits were cultivated there. These require year-round water for the most part, and some four acre feet of irrigation water per season. This is not an unusual sequence on irrigated lands; from extensive cropping to more intensive land uses.

Another change from the first plans of irrigation projects consistently develops in the west. During a few wet seasons there may be more water than is needed to fill the reservoirs and ditches of a project. In blind hopefulness or downright craftiness land speculators extend "fringe" irrigation canals that never carry water in any but the years of abundant precipitation. This "fringe" of super-submarginal irrigated land showed up in the Salt River basin.

When surface water became grievously short someone

found that natural rainfall and irrigation had stored many millions of acre feet of water in the ground beneath fields of this project. Well-pumping began; started before 1940, well drilling was rampant in the Salt River project after World War II. With no adequate ground-water program or law, wells were sunk at will. By 1944 giant pumps were drawing nearly a half million acre feet of water from aquifers that was in excess of the recharge rate. The tilled and watered fields were extravagantly overextended. The gamblers who "mined" the aquifers saw the necessity for public money to rescue them from their folly. A first try at getting Congress to underwrite a project that threatened to cost over two billion dollars to benefit mostly some 400 owners of irrigated fields failed. Then the "tin roof" movement which came into the open in 1956 (first talked about by livestock interests much earlier) began to be ballyhooed.

Promoters of the tin-roof scheme proposed that pines, the junipers we call cedar, and other trees be cut off the mountain slopes. Trees demand water for their growth so out they were to go. In some of the propaganda there was the very extreme suggestion that a portion of the slopes be made "impervious"—that means *paved!* But for the most part, the idea was to do away with the forests and, by man's command, shift to grass cover—on the theory that grass would require less moisture and let more precipitation rush down hill to the reservoirs.

The irrigation people who had driven wells at such a headlong pace could not escape the appeal of several hundred thousand more acre feet of water delivered into the reservoirs. However spurious the reasoning that made them believe they would get this water, they embraced the scheme.

But questions such as these seemed almost to shout with caution as the ballyhoo for tin-roofing the Salt River watershed mounted:

Would grass take less moisture for growth than a mixture of evergreens, shrubs, and grasses? If "proof" is offered that a grass slope in another region will deliver more water, does it apply in Arizona?

Would the livestock interests that seem to have first proposed this tin-roof watershed management for national-forest lands in Arizona let their herds eat grass to the crowns to prevent the leaves from transpiring a greater proportion of the precipitation? That could be the hidden menace of this bizarre tin-roof proposal, the reckless grazing of the grasses.

Then, if the livestock people did succeed in such a great conversion from forest cover to grass cover, and the grass was heavily grazed to prevent it from using water, what assurance may we have that the shallow, unshaded roots will not be baked out, the grass die, the binding power of the fibrous roots be lost? If that should happen, little stringer gullies the size of your finger would begin to dig channels which eventually would be deep and wide enough to hold a house. Erosion would slash the hills, and we would have that many more acres of scalded desert which once were sufficiently timbered to be included in a forest.

Within the memory of conservationists it is probable that no proposal with regard to management, mismanagement, or sly exploitation has had such long-range vicious potentials in destroying the natural wealth inherent in the basic soil as this one has. The greatest menace lies in the fact that for a few years a denuded watershed, a tin roof, may deliver more water to downstream dams than the one with forest cover which makes the rain and snow water "walk down hill" instead of rush headlong. If this is "proven" in Arizona, it may be duplicated in many other watersheds.

Desperate as some areas of the western third of the nation are for water, local boomers, seeing only the immediate results, would again and again take up the banners for this utterly fallacious proposal with all of its slick dress-up of more water for thirsty acres. Forests grow on and protect tender soils. Man's tampering with the protective cover is too much of a risk for any community dependent on a good watershed to take.

V I

You'll find a distinctive odor in the air in many parts of Region 3. When it is mostly the slow-eddying smoke from piñon-pine fires in humble dwellings along the upper Rio Grande, or anywhere I encounter that fragrance, I think of it as incense. But when it tickles in the nostrils it has a slight sting, and it is predominantly a smell of dust, bringing to mind the whole panorama of the desert and its green islands in the mountains. There is comfort in the thought that if sound forest management prevails, the slopes of these hills will be green and the streams, so vital to the lowlands, will flow more constantly and with less sediment in them.

But there are specters in this panorama. This is, after all, desert. Fundamentally it is desert because there has been so little rain over recent centuries that the land has lost all but that vegetation attuned to not only days, but also successive years of drought. Probably as many acres—and perhaps more—are desert today than were desert a century ago, because more livestock grazed on the tender, critical slopes than should have been allowed.

This cannot be repeated too often; there is a genuine, renewable resource value in the forage grown within the national forests. The one economical commerical method of *harvest* of this crop is by grazing domestic animals on it. There is a point where such grazing must halt: at the point that will allow enough of the growth of grasses and forbs to remain so that these stems and leaves will maintain enough of a soil sponge in top soil to insure its permeability for watershed values and better growing-conditions for the forage plants themselves.

This grazing use, because of the hullabaloo that flared up during the efforts of certain livestock operators to put over the "Great Land Grab" on the national forests, has been emphasized far above its actual position in forest management and wealth. Here are fairly recent data that indicate the relationship between the timber and the grazing values deriving from our forests: in 1955 the income from timber sales in all the national forests totaled $73,187,364.10; in the same period grazing fees for all forests totaled $2,953,257.54.

Or consider what the showing is in Region 3, where there has been a constant drive on the part of a few stockmen to achieve some type of "Land Grab" by legislation. These now are tied in with this tin-roof brainstorm, which actually may be a scheme fostered by land-greedy stockmen with the irrigationists as a big, enthusiastic claque.

In 1955 in Arizona and New Mexico timber operators paid $2,253,645.54 for "stumpage" on national forests and stockmen paid $611,961.15 for grazing privileges on the forests.

The time may come—if it is not yet here—when it will be of much more importance to let the grassy stuff that forest acres produce fall back to the ground unharvested to protect critical soils and watersheds than to produce the relatively few pounds of beef and mutton resulting from grazing on national-forest allotments.

VII

WHEN traveling in New Mexico across Glorietta Pass on U.S. Highways 84 and 85, be sure to look at the slopes on either side of the road. There are gullies and there is sheet erosion of the red soil, now fully exposed and all mineral with no grass roots or stems to hold it together. The land immediately beside the road is not in a national forest, but only a few hundred yards on either side of the highway in many of its stretches, the Santa Fe National Forest spreads to the skyline. Or if you drive along U.S. 84 south of Las Vegas, New Mexico, you will see land made bankrupt by overgrazing during years gone by. Only where piñon pine, the juniper trees, and the brushy bushes grow will you see any grassy growth, any remnant of protective top soil. The trees and shrubs stand on little pedestals with a collar of grass around their bases, the soil between the woody plants all worn and washed away.

Look beside the road as you follow U.S. 66 or U.S. 89 in the vicinity of Flagstaff, Arizona. Look as you travel a little way on U.S. 60 through the Tonto National Forest near Globe and Miami, Arizona. This is part of the country proposed for tin-roof watershed management. Can it fare better than those wrecked lands I have cited?

This western mountain land is tender. This land is in national forest, and it should remain so. And when it may be grazed, it must be so carefully used as to protect the tender body of the soil. That is the positive, mandatory consideration in the legitimate use of national-forest lands used for grazing of domestic stock.

Perhaps there is just one more quality I should emphasize about Region 3. It has not only its fragrance, but it is luminous with a beauty and allure that surely will capture you, at least for a while, and perhaps for the rest of your life. This would be a desolate stretch of country if it were not for the mountains—and on their sides are the national forests we have established to keep these high islands and their delivery of clear water at a high level of productivity.

VIII

A BASIN FILLED WITH BIG ROCKS

I

A TYPE of curiosity near Christmas time demonstrates itself in the hefting of packages and the shaking of them to see if they rattle. The dimensions of a package particularly prod one's curiosity, as one tries to learn what is inside.

In a similar way, the dimensions of a forest region or a forest within it, lead to wondering what may be found in its acres, square miles, and townships. If your curiosity is tweaked by the size of a package, you will be intrigued by the tremendous acreage of the Intermountain Region, Region 4, of the U.S. Forest Service.

Region 4 is so large it poses a question as to where and how we should start tracing its boundaries. I do know one way to start.

While working on a survey of mountain land an old-timer engineer showed me this trick of back-country transit handling. Lacking official landmarks he would drive a stake, number it o-plus-oo, and start his field notes with "Beginning at a point—." Then he'd tie "the point" to a handy tree, rock, or mountain.

So: "Beginning at a point on U.S. Highway 93, approximately 92 miles south of Missoula, Montana . . ."

You are now on Lost Trail Pass and 6,951 feet above sea level. Montana and Region 1 lie to the north; Idaho and Region 4 to the south. The Pass is on the Continental Divide northwest from Yellowstone Park, in the Bitterroot

Mountains. North and east are streams running toward the Missouri; south and west they drain through the Snake to the Columbia River.

Start here to traverse Region 4 by the most direct route to the farthest point south in this region and you soon encounter well-known tourist attractions. At Dickey, Idaho, you have an option. Bearing to the east you approach the Craters of the Moon National Monument. Trending westerly you arrive in Sun Valley where the upper reaches of the famous Bald Mountain ski run is within the Sawtooth National Forest. And that very famous wilderness of the Middle Fork of the Salmon River is over the hill from the basin holding Sun Valley.

The canyon of the Snake River, its waterfalls, and the "Thousand Springs," where underground rivers break out of lava cliffs to pour into the Snake, are near this route. Then, in Nevada, the north-south ranges of mountains flank the highway, and you see forest cover that in terms of lumber production is scrub, but as protection to watersheds is priceless. Finally you come into the fabulous, neon-flamed street known as The Strip, in a town bearing the Spanish name that means "The Fruitful Plains." Even then, as you travel on from Las Vegas, you pass Henderson with its gigantic war-spawned magnesium plants, Boulder City, Hoover Dam, the reservoir above it, and the road then leads on for nearly a hundred desert-bordered miles before you reach the southmost point of Region 4.

Should you choose a less direct and longer route to the east of U.S. 93, you would pass through Ogden, Salt Lake City, Cedar City, and swing into southern Nevada to arrive at Las Vegas. Along either route, those mountains that have any woody growth on them are most likely within Region 4's forests. By the shortest of these two routes the miles traveled would approximate 1,000; by the longer one, perhaps you would tally nearly 1,500 miles.

Another type of measurement can be applied to this stretch between Lost Trail Pass and the point of Nevada's wedge-shaped southern tip. On the pass trees are those you would encounter at sea level near the Yukon. South of Hoover Dam roads are bordered by Joshua trees, palo-verde trees, fishhook cactus, and ocotillo—desert flora.

More graphic still might be the fact that the distance north to south in Region 4 would approximate that between Des Moines, Iowa, and Boston, Massachusetts, or between Atlanta, Georgia, and Montreal, Quebec.

East to west across the northern portion of Region 4 you measure your mileage from Togwotee Pass in the Wind River Mountains east of Jackson Hole, Wyoming, to the Snake River where it is the Idaho-Oregon boundary. Farther south the Manti-Lasal National Forest pokes a finger across Colorado's line toward Paradox Valley. From this small dab of the region in Colorado Region 4 reaches to the eastern shore of Lake Tahoe and across the eastern boundary of California. Either of those east-west distances may be measured best as two days of vacation travel. U.S. highways 30, 40, 50, and 6 twist and dodge as they find routes through a clutter of mountains, and hours are a truer gauge of travel time than mileage.

The dimensions of this region are thus indicated, though not tightly drawn. In other instances I have been able to offer a recollection that served as a keynote beyond which the composition of a region unrolled. I have no one place, hour, and impression to offer to introduce the intermountain region; many memories rise as units of a magnificent panorama. To "begin at a point," I can start at the Hole among the Wyoming mountains named in honor of William Sublette's partner, David Jackson.

Famous Jackson Hole is an anchor point at the northeast corner of Region 4. Those mighty peaks to the west of the Hole—named *"Les Trois Tetons"* by French trappers about the year 1800—and the main valley floor are in the Grand Teton National Park. But all around the park are national forests.

Here in the Hole is a traffic hub of early and historically significant western travel. In August 1807 John Colter, an Army enlisted man, secured his release from Lewis and Clark as the expedition returned to the Missouri, then joined the trappers Joseph Dickson and Forrest Hancock to reap peltry in Jackson Hole. Alone throughout most of that winter, Colter traversed this area, the first white man to see Yellowstone's hot springs, geysers, and other phenomena.

In the autumn of the next year, trapping near the Jefferson river with John Potts, a former expedition companion, Colter made his fabulous run to freedom. The two men encountered a band of Blackfoot Indians. Potts killed a brave and was riddled with arrows. Colter was stripped, turned loose to run for his life, which he did toward the Jefferson river, six miles away. He turned on his nearest pursuer, wrenched a spear from the Indian's hands, killed the Blackfoot, gained the river, hid near a beaver house, and that night he set out to cover 300 miles to Manuel Lisa's fort on the Missouri. He made it, sun-blistered, scratched, foot-weary, and nigh done-for.

Colter was the first publicist of this region, and he did it the hard way. People didn't believe him when he told about the geysers and hot springs; the first name applied to our Yellowstone Park, and applied derisively, was "Colter's Hell."

Through Jackson Hole traveled trappers of the Hudson Bay Company, the Astorians, the Mountain Men working with or for the Sublettes, Fitzpatrick, Carson, Smith, and Bridger. Though many of the valleys, ridges, and passes within the national forests surrounding Jackson Hole may appear as if there never had been other than Indian moccasins tracking the trails, there probably were shaggy whiskered men of fair complexions using these travel lines some years before Illinois and Indiana were admitted to statehood.

Eastward from Jackson Hole is the Teton National Forest. If you follow the trails toward the Continental Divide, which here is the ridge of the Wind River Mountains, you traverse a constantly up-sloping mass of earth crust which has a sudden drop-off to the east—the escarpment of the Wind River range. We looked on these cliffs from Chauvenet Peak in the Shoshone forest. In the northeast part of the Teton forest is the "Thorofare country," where the great elk herds that often have totaled 7,000 head come out of Yellowstone National Park, which is their summer range, and drift down through the Teton National Forest to Jackson Hole. Here they seek the "Elk Ranch" of the U.S. Fish & Wildlife Service, where they eke out the last bit of winter crisis.

Also in the Teton National Forest are the 885 square miles of the Teton Wilderness Area. Within this wildland sanctuary you may visit Two Ocean Pass, where a small lake in a mountain saddle has two outlets, one flowing into Yellowstone and Missouri River drainage by way of Atlantic Creek, the other to the Snake and thence to the Columbia via Pacific Creek.

If you face west at many points in the Teton Forest you see *Les Trois Tetons* in their most dramatic setting. Like a great stone wave breaking against a hard, invisible cliff of mountain atmosphere, the Tetons toss high above the valley floor. Standing at the base of these spectacular mountains, you are so close to their sheared faces that it is difficult for sight and mind to measure their height and bulk. Viewing them from a spot in the national forest, across the intervening valley, presents them splendidly.

A little distance south of Jackson Hole are mountains within the Bridger National Forest. Jim Bridger was even more celebrated as a frontiersman than Jackson. A Virginian who operated a ferry boat in his native state before becoming a blacksmith in Saint Louis, he then came west in 1822 as a member of the Henry-Ashley troop of Mountain Men. He merits a forest bearing his name.

The two other forests supplying guardian wildlands encircling the Grand Teton National Park are the Targhee and the Caribou—strange names, particularly the one of an animal so far south of its native range. A bit of research uncovers their origins.

The first one, Targhee, comes from the Bannock Indians. The Bannocks are related to the Shoshones, and, like the tribe of Sacajawea and Washakie, the Bannocks did not make war on the whitemen as did the Cheyennes, Sioux, and Apaches. Targhee was a Bannock chieftain. He seems to have a modest right to recognition by the circumstances surrounding at least one of his several reported deaths. One version relates he was killed in battle with the Crow Indians in Montana in 1871. Another version tells of Targhee fighting on the side of the U.S. Troops, and relates that he died at the hands of Nez Percé warriors in the battle of Shotgun Valley in 1877, six years later. For the most part the Indians who have been most publicized are the warriors: the Sitting Bulls, the Geronimos, and the Josephs. Though Washakie lost his national-forest memorial by its consolidation with the Shoshone, Targhee, also a "good Indian," still has a forest commemorating his name.

The Caribou National Forest—now it is certain there never were any of these animals in this locality! But inquiry reveals that if we should be entirely on the side of accuracy perhaps this should be the Jesse Fairchild National Forest. Fairchild was also known as "Caribou Jack." He got the name by telling tall tales of his exploits in the far north. This Jack did discover gold in the Caribou Valley of southeastern Idaho, the valley did acquire his nickname because of this, and by the next step "Caribou" did become the name of the 1,010,000-acre national forest.

Names and history continually entrap us on national forests of the west as they did on forests of the east. We have staked down one corner of the region; perhaps we may do something similar by brief mentions of the region's other three corners, and then fill in here and there so that we can put together a sketch-outline of this big Intermountain Region.

II

AT THE southeast corner of Region 4 is the 1,339,449-acre Manti-Lasal National Forest. Manti is the name of a city mentioned in the Book of Mormon and was selected by Brigham Young for a town in southern Utah. Originally there were two forests here; the Manti and the Lasal.

In the Manti division of the combined forest is one of those warnings that shout "Beware" at interests such as those in Arizona, which in 1957 became radical proponents of the tin-roof watershed. This case history of what happens when critical slopes are overgrazed is at Mount Pleasant, Utah, in the San Pitch Valley.

A little mountain-born stream, Pleasant Creek, runs through Mount Pleasant. At one time it must have been a clear brook, probably supporting a fair population of trout. It probably had a fairly constant year-round flow from springs that got their water from melting snows and summer showers. Snowmelt and pouring rain were caught by herbage and ground litter so most of the precipitation soaked into the ground to come out again through the springs. Early settlers named the creek "Pleasant."

But, like many creeks that have suffered from destruction of ground cover, this stream became "ugly." Probably only a few local people noticed that about a tenth of the 17,000 acres in the basin which collected the flow of Pleasant Creek had been skinned down to mineral soil, and that the basin had become in part a tin-roof watershed.

On the afternoon of June 19, 1918, a thunderhead that developed into a typical western cloudburst rolled in above the watershed of Pleasant Creek. The bottom dropped out of the clouds; the creek filled with angry waters and came roaring into Mount Pleasant, trundling boulders as big as jeeps down the main street. A farmer drowned, debris covered lawns, basements were flooded, fences were wrecked, and fields and gardens were ruined. The damage amounted to $100,000.

On July 9, 1918, at 8:00 P.M., Pleasant Creek again suffered a major flood.

On July 30, 1936, another big flood hit. Irrigation ditches were ruined, city water mains washed out, crops damaged, and roads destroyed.

Then came July 24, 1946. That date, July 24, has a special meaning for members of the Church of Latter Day Saints. It is the day when the first settlers of their faith arrived in the valley of the Great Salt Lake. People of the Mount Pleasant community readied for a gala celebration. They decked the town with flags and bunting. The parade was to begin soon after 4:00 P.M., but before it could get moving, the storm hit. The whole story of a cloudburst and a tin-roof watershed was repeated.

That flood originated on *only about* 1,700 *acres* of the total watershed's 17,000 acres. The rate of travel of the flood was clocked at from 8 to 12 miles per hour. Samples of flood flow showed that *25 to 60 per cent by volume was sediment.* The bared land at the head of the basin not only rushed the water down, but it tossed into the racing water from a quarter to over a half of the flood's volume the vulnerable soil washed from the hillsides.

At a cost of $40 per acre, local, state, and federal agencies terraced, contour-trenched, and reseeded the 1,700 acres of "tin roof" to give it a new, *flood-preventing* thatch. The lesson of what happens when a western watershed is denuded even in only a small part of the whole was costly for Mount Pleasant, Utah. Other communities can profit by the lesson only by giving heed to what it demonstrated.

The Lasal part of the combined forest contains the most southeasterly portion of Region 4. It is near the "Four Corners Country" where four states share a common point on their boundaries. Here are famous natural bridges, the Navaho Indians, and a recent uranium mining-stampede. This is the major center of our uranium production. Long before that, the radium used by the Curies in their experiments came out of Colorado, from the area between the Lasal forest of Region 4 and the Uncompahgre forest of Region 2.

Until the uranium rush whipped across this part of the west, and the leaping jeeps raced over the sage flats like ground-hugging tumbleweeds, this was probably the least populated, most roadless part of the nation. It still is anything but subdued.

Continuing clockwise, turning west from the Four Corners, we next steer a course to that point where Nevada's boundary, running due south from a point on the Oregon line, shifts to a course that lies southeasterly. West of Carson City, Nevada's capital, north of this point where the boundary angles, the east shore of Lake Tahoe is both in Nevada and in the Toiyabe National Forest. And near the angle of the boundary shared with California, 700,000 acres of Region 4 forest lie in the Golden State.

Here in the southern portion of California's famed Sierra Madre, in the forest called Toiyabe, which in Indian language means "Black Mountains," is the southwest anchor post of Region 4.

At the northwest portion of Region 4 is the Payette National Forest. The forest bears the name of the local river, its valley, and the near-by town. The forest name, of course, came from that of the valley, river, and town.

But where did the name "Payette" originate?

On October 20, 1818, Great Britain and the young United States entered into an almost forgotten treaty. The Russians, the Spanish, and the English all had set foot on rocks and beaches throughout the northwest country, proclaiming their several rulers' ownership of vast and unknown lands. With Lewis and Clark, another main contender for sovereignty over this region entered the scene.

Fur companies were racing to see which might get the upper hand. The claims and citizens of Britain and the United States began to meet head on in serious conflict. The 1818 treaty merely postponed the decision as to who might finally take title to this empire. As Bancroft wrote, each of these nations "reserved the right to quarrel at a later date, and under favorable circumstances, should the country prove worth the trouble."

In that same year the Hudson's Bay Company hired a

young French-Canadian, who joined those who moved westward into this unsettled domain. The young men so engaged became the staffs at trading-posts and forts where valuable peltry could be gathered. One of the Hudson's Bay Company stations was Fort Boise. A first fort in this location was built by John Reed, who was killed by Indians in 1814. A second fort founded about 1820 by Donald Mackenzie was short-lived. The Company built Fort Boise in 1834, moved it to a better site in 1838, and finally after it was partially destroyed by flood in 1853 abandoned it in 1855.

The young French-Canadian hired in 1818 was named François Payette. He advanced in rank and responsibility until, in 1837, he became "Master" at Fort Boise. He was a kindly man, offering all he could to aid and comfort those mile-weary travelers of the Oregon Trail who stopped at his station. Among the many to whom he was hospitable were members of the Reverend Marcus Whitman's party.

The river, valley, town, national forest, and even the Payette-Boise Lumber Company, whose signs are well known in western states, all bear his name. The 2,418,977-acre Payette National Forest is the northwesterly bastion of Region 4; adjacent to it is the 2,950,613-acre Boise National Forest, one of several Idaho features perpetuating the name of Payette's frontier station.

III

HAVING established corners, let us examine what lies interior to them.

After three or more decades during which the Mountain

Men became familiar with the West, that intrepid explorer J. C. Frémont arrived and gave the body of Region 4 its misleading name. He called it "The Great Basin." A recently published encyclopedia persists in describing the area as extending from the "west wall" of the Rockies to the "east wall" of the Sierra Madre. The inference is that it is a basin with flat country between the two mountain systems.

The description might be correct except for one thing. Measuring 300 to 500 miles east to west, the "basin" is chock full of sizable rock-sided mountains. Included here is the major mountain range called Wasatch. These tumbled uplands have been fashioned along with heights both south and north, by what I think of as "The Big Slip."

Though we may have thought briefly of the White, Green, Great Smoky, and Blue Ridge mountains as continually changing, we quickly revert to thinking of the "eternal hills" as being immutable and unchanging. For many, the Rockies and the associated ranges are the ultimate symbol of immovability. But Region 4 offers The Big Slip as an active demonstration of how restless parts of the Rockies may be.

Earthquakes do occur in the east. Reelfoot Lake in Tennessee formed in a 20-mile-long depression after an earthquake of 1812. Many remember more recent earthquakes that shook Helena, Montana, in 1935. But most often we think of movements along the San Andreas Fault and its extensions. This is the fault responsible for many ripples in the earth's skin in southern California.

I experienced one of those San Andreas shivers at 6:33 A.M., on February 9, 1956. The earth quaked several times at La Jolla that morning. Well over a hundred lesser tremors and shakes were recorded in the following weeks; some of these were mildly noticeable, others went unnoticed as we got accustomed to the land trembling a little. An average of three and a half quakes per day are recorded in Japan, but they get no general notice.

Rarely is there any mention of earthquakes along The Big Slip; local residents are accustomed to the earth's little adjustments. Regardless of this lack of notoriety, a tremendous line of slippage is located along a line from the great escarpment of Glacier National Park to far down in the Grand Canyon country. The quake that shook Helena was part of the slipping that takes place along this north-south line.

You have looked from the Teton National Forest toward the eastern face of the Grand Teton and its neighboring peaks. The east face of those peaks is a part of this "Slip." At Salt Lake City look eastward and you see the Wasatch Mountains. Now and again there is an unnoticed shaking of the ground and the tremendous mass of those mountains acquires a few finger-widths of additional height above the Salt Lake Valley floor.

Such wrinkling, sinking, lifting, and tearing down by climate have filled Mr. Frémont's "Great Basin" with north-and-south ridges. There is one nonconforming mountain chain named the Uinta, located in the Ashley National Forest in northeastern Utah. It has been called the only range of its size extending along an east-west axis. The highest point is King's Peak, 13,948 feet above sea level. Here also is the 243,957-acre High Uintas Primitive Area, set aside in 1931 to preserve its wilderness values.

As in all locations, the mountains of the Great Basin are cloud traps. The verdure of fields, gardens, and home grounds you see at Ogden and Salt Lake City, at Twin Falls and around the great potato center of Burley, Idaho, the peach orchards of Brigham City, Provo, and St. George in Utah, the Washoe River that runs brightly through

Reno to disappear in the Carson Sink—there would be no such oases if there were no cloud-robbing mountain peaks. But long ago this Great Basin was anything but desert. It held two gigantic, fresh-water lakes.

Today, near Reno, Nevada, there are three sizable lakes: Pyramid, Winnemucca, and Walker. They are what is left of the gigantic, fresh-water inland sea that shimmered here when glacial ice spread far south over North America. That lost lake was given the name of Louis Armand, Baron de Lahontan, one of Du Lhut's associates, who wrote in 1703 of partly imagined explorations in the far west. He wrote particularly of a "Long River," which many who came later tried to find and never did, for like Lake Lahontan, it had a facility for vanishing.

In the same period when Lake Lahontan spread over much of what is now Nevada, the Great Salt Lake was a tremendous spread of sweet water which had its outlet to the valley of the Snake River through the Bear River canyon of northern Utah. So recently did this fresh-water lake exist that you may look eastward from any point along the fertile belt between the Great Salt Lake and foothills of the Wasatch Mountains, and you will see the ancient high-water line.

In these Wasatch foothills is probably the most spectacular demonstration of the interrelation of vegetal cover and run-off that can be found in America. This is the site of the Davis County floods. They are, on a grand scale, a giant replica of the floods that plagued Mount Pleasant farther to the south.

Grazing of cattle and sheep began on these hills soon after the first Mormon settlement. By 1877 smaller floods gave warning watersheds were being abused. The lands that were to produce the devastating floods became private property. They were leased each season to owners of sheep.

The herders proceeded to utilize every last bit of forage procurable. Brush was burned off in the belief it would assure more forage. While they rated as floods, the several muddy washes that occurred in earlier periods were small compared with the one that finally hit on August 14, 1923, and another that came roaring out of the foothills on July 10, 1930. These were climaxes.

I saw the aftermath of one of those major floods. The road crews had bulldozed a corridor with five-foot walls through the mud and rock that had spewed over the highway near Bountiful, Utah. On the downward side of the road was a house. Flood junk had piled in against it to within three feet of the eaves; a big boulder about one third the size of a standard boxcar was part of that detritus. From this point near the canyon portal, the muck fanned for several miles out over the fertile, high-priced truck-crop lands—muck about three feet deep and coarse at the base near the foothills, to only an inch or so of microscopic clay particles at its farthest extension. This sterile sheet of junk lay over soil of good tilth and rich nutrients and had to be skimmed off before more crops could be grown.

Studies showed that the floods originated from a tin-roof condition caused by overgrazing plus burning of protective ground cover. Only 17 per cent of the total watershed area delivered the flood crests. The people of Ogden and Salt Lake City, led by alert service clubs, raised the money to buy these skinned lands and donated them to the nation to be administered by the U.S. Forest Service.

When Civilian Conservation Corps labor and projects became available in the 1930s, these abused slopes were terraced, replanted, and healed. A few years after ground cover had been re-established, a storm dumped nine inches of rain on these slopes. There were no floods. The streams ran high but clear.

The Davis County floods present the full cycle of man's misuse of western mountain watersheds; the tin-roof watershed has been fully tried out here and consigned to Limbo.

I V

IN THE western third of the nation 155,000,000 acres in national forests and approximately 145,000,000 acres now in "Grazing Districts," are our citizen-owned wildlife lands. With some 300,000,000 acres devoted to wildlife, it would seem as if there would be no question about adequate space for the wildlings. So the statement that thousands of deer, and in some locations elk and bighorn sheep, have starved to death because of too great a population on their hereditary range may cause shock—and questioning.

More than a few of these "population explosions" have occurred on western game ranges. Suddenly there are two animals demanding the space and food that will take care of one; suddenly there are even more than two, and soon there is a die-off. That is nature's way of balancing population with sustaining habitat—and it is a rough and stern method. For even among those wobbly animals that survive winter and start the staggering trek toward summer pastures in the highlands, many never reach the spruce-guarded valleys where fawns and elk calves are born. Predators "take" them.

Supposedly informed people have said: "Predators perform a good service; they clean old, weak, and sick animals out of the herds."

But those people could not have seen—as I have seen—approximately 22,500 deer in one herd, all weakened by ill-advised feeding of ground alfalfa and stock-foot pellets, beginning the slow, dragging climb back to high valleys as spring green tinted the hills. They could not have seen the snowy record of how a struggling deer was hazed into an area of crusted snow where coyotes could run on the top and deer would break through. You know by the sign in the snow that the snow-trapped deer squalled and struggled and died while the dog's wild relatives tore at shreds of quivering flesh and sang of the kill. Other deer, hundreds of them in that poor herd, filled bellies with unsuited food, staggered a few rods from feed troughs, collapsed, and died of malnutrition. Only where game and natural food for it are in balance will healthy herds be found.

That is a grisly picture, but a true one. Gradually we learn. Now we employ applied good sense and call it game management. It is a term of relatively recent coinage. In simple language game management is animal husbandry, such as any farmer may practice, applied to wild livestock. With wild or domestic stock, herds must be kept within the carrying capacity of the pasturage available. Applied to big game, this requires hunting as the one practical tool to maintain a balance between food and animals.

The population explosions among deer herds of the west caught western game-and-fish-department officials off balance. A series of actions on the part of officials and sportsmen set the forces in motion that culminated in these almost unbelievable recent years of overabundance in game animals.

From the days of early settlement until a little while after 1900 western game populations declined to grievous scarcity. After World War I the old Biological Survey launched wholesale war by bullet, trap, and poison against wolves, coyotes, cougars, and bears. Wolves were entirely rubbed out in some western states; coyotes then became Biological Survey's principal target.

Predators had been a considerable natural check on the depleted big-game populations. A mature cougar demands about two full-grown deer a week as his fare. Hunting seasons were abandoned completely in some states, and this further added breeding stock to base herds.

In the late 1920s, a "refuge program" spread throughout the west. State legislatures drew lines, composed texts, and in a chorus of "Ayes," closed to all hunting a half-million acres in dozens of places within national forest and on similar publicly-owned wildlands. Quite a few of those refuges were so large that deer could be born, and could live, breed, and die within them without ever being subject to hunting. The refuges added a powerful factor to the rapid increase of deer herds.

When hunting seasons were opened, the "buck law" prevailed. Only antlered deer could be hunted. Does were "sacred cows," so to speak. But so long as the ratio remained, at the time of the rut, one mature buck to as many as a dozen female deer, there would be fawns the following spring—a single the first year, twins for each bred doe thereafter so long as she was fertile.

All these factors were at work near the end of World War I, and, moreover, sizable areas existed into which roads suitable for auto travel had not been built. Few hunters got into such areas even if they were outside of refuges and open to hunting. One such area, combining most of these factors favorable to rampant upsurge once populations began pyramiding, was the Kaibab Plateau in the national forest north of the Grand Canyon in Arizona.

After catastrophe had hit the Kaibab, investigators esti-

mated that if the deer herd could have been stabilized at
32,000 head, with 8,000 or so harvested each year, that
status of animals and adequate forage could have continued indefinitely. But wrangling started at the very out-
set when this became a crisis deer-herd area. The clash
came between state officials responsible for administering
laws related to game and federal officials charged with
protecting lands and what grows on them from receiving
a beating from fire, insects, cows, or deer. And while the
wrangling went on, the deer population on the Kaibab
surged to 100,000 head and over. Then as nature applied
her drastic correctives, the population dropped to 10,000
head or less—nobody really determined how low those
numbers did dip. But the massive die-off let both the
damaged range and the decimated deer herd begin to work
toward rehabilitation.

Lessons were learned from the Kaibab catastrophe.

V

In July 1943 I visited Utah's "Dixie" and the pleasant
mountain area that had the commonplace name of Fishlake National Forest. Here is one of several places where
lessons learned on the Kaibab National Forest have saved
other forest game herds from calamity.

At midnight our party had scurried across the deep
earth-dimple, Death Valley. We paused only to sleep
briefly at Las Vegas, Nevada, then glanced at the Hoover
Dam, looked fleetingly at the Grand Canyon, and finally
descended from the north side of the Kaibab Plateau to
arrive at Zion National Park. Afterglow had lingered on the
park's central scenic attraction, the Great White Throne,

as we crawled into bedrolls, and at daybreak the Throne glowed again against the dawn sky.

Ross Leonard, then Director of the Utah Fish & Game Department, was our guide during our brief tour of Utah's Dixie, and he met us as we struck out from the overnight stop in Zion. In a mountain-girt land cove surrounding St. George town, which is in the center of this "Dixie," fruit and truck crops are ahead of those grown in the northern part of the state by some sixty days. Though some Utahans declare the climate is "semi-tropical," it is not quite that. In this area the Latter Day Saints did grow their own cotton, and that certainly gives it the right to be called Dixie (Western Division).

Heading north from Zion following U.S. Highway 91 through Cedar City, we soon saw cedar trees "high-lined" by deer eating as high as they could reach and the knotty witch-broom ends of the mountain mahogany where deer had so constantly nibbled that only the stubby, hard, woody butt ends of twigs were left in clusters; there was no new growth. No more evidence was needed to prove that Fishlake National Forest had a deer problem.

Winter range is big game's crisis area in the west and such range is located in the low country. In former days, before fences, ranches, highways, dogs, men, and guns moved into the lower valleys and the great sage-and-grass country, game herds traversed many miles in the migration from high forest valleys to wintering grounds. Today there is one herd, that of the White River National Forest, where deer find low country open enough to move seasonally as they did long ago. From Shingle Peak in the White River wilderness area to the Utah line is a hundred miles or more by the deer trails. But the first full moon following the first high-country snow sees this herd, still numbering about 35,000, moving almost in a sheet mi-

gration to the open sage, cedar, and piñon wintering areas
west of this forest. Other herds stack up on greatly
limited areas, often "public domain," between forest
boundaries and ranches. Winter range now used by deer
is only a fraction of what was available years ago.

If all types of animals grazing our national forests are
kept in balance with the available forage species they
prefer, there is no great competition between cows and
deer, elk and sheep. Each class of forage-eating livestock,
domestic and wild, has priorities in preference, mostly
different from the other species on the same range. When
all animals are driven to eating anything to fill their bellies,
then they do come in all-out competition.

And the situation had become crucially competitive in
the summer of 1943, when I visited the Dixie and Fishlake
national-forest ranges with Ross Leonard. The deer populations were snowballing.

But here state and forest men were fore-armed, and intelligent management planning and action was being applied. Here is a brief history of what happened in relation
to "the deer problem" on the Fishlake, a representative
southern Utah national forest in Region 4.

V I

WHEN the Utah Game and Fish Department was established in 1894, and for about a decade and a half after
that long "open" seasons for hunting, lasting up to six
months, were the rule. No requirement for a hunting
license existed until 1907. No effective law enforcement
was maintained. By 1908 the herds of big game were
so depleted that a five-year closure on elk, deer, and big-

horns was decreed by state action. From the very few deer that were in the base herds at this time, there was enough increase so that a bucks-only open season of 15 days was set in 1913. Then followed the period of the "buck law," the big game refuges, the predators killed at the behest of stockmen.

In 1916 rangers reported a total of 8,400 deer on all national forests in Utah. In 1917 it was estimated that 2,600 deer were on the Fishlake National Forest.

With an estimated 3,000 deer on the Fishlake in 1920, hunting began and sportsmen took 10 per cent of the herd. But those taken were bucks. Protected does continued to increase and bear fawns. To further intensify the oncoming explosion in deer population, Utah in 1925 established 11 state game preserves, with nearly a million acres of these within the national forests. In 1925 an estimated 6,500 head of deer lived on the Fishlake National Forest. Five years later, *the deer population on the Fishlake had reached 20,500 head.*

There *had* to be an "antlerless season." This herd was plunging into a run-away increase. It took four years to get sportsmen and others to agree to that doe season. The Fishlake deer herd then numbered an estimated 32,000. That was in 1934. Permits for 500 antlerless deer were issued. That was not enough. By next year the deer population jumped from 32,000 to 35,250. There had been nearly 5,000 kills the year before, but most of these were bucks. Only 1,050 antlerless permits had been issued. Newspapers, sportsmen, various groups campaigned against doe-killing so emphatically that antlerless permits were discontinued in 1936 and 1937. People said: "You've solved the deer problem; don't shoot any more does!"

From 35,250 estimated deer on the Fishlake in 1935, the figure jumped to 39,000 in 1936, then to 43,000 in

1937. The Fishlake was all triggered to repeat the tragedy of the Kaibab.

The state game officials knew they had to act. In 1938 2,500 antlerless permits were authorized on the Fishlake forest. A greater furore began. "Don't shoot does!" If you did, you were a low-principled scoundrel. As a result of this hullabaloo the sale of the antlerless permits was disheartening. Many hysterical Protectors of the Does bought permits and tore them up or burned them—to the delight of news photographers. The deer population jumped again: from 43,000 to 50,000 in the ensuing 12 months.

As on the Kaibab, where it had been estimated by wildlife experts that the range could have maintained for all time a herd of 32,000 head, the Fishlake was appraised as having about the same carrying capacity. Deer population was about once and a half the numbers the range would support. Because of the sportsmen's and sentimentalists' opposition, the increase was now in full gear. But the level-headed populace for the most part finally saw the pattern, saw it as a repeat of the great die-off on the near-by Kaibab. When the population hit 50,000 head, 6,000 antlerless permits were authorized, 5,930 *were purchased*, and at a phenomenal level, 5,300 of the purchasers were successful in bagging a doe.

The year before we traveled through the Fishlake country, the total population of deer on that national forest reached 56,000. But in that year 20,000 *antlerless permits were issued for this one forest.* Of these 19,147 were sold; 15,700 of them were "filled."

It was drastic action; *it had to be drastic!*

That was the critical high point in deer population on the Fishlake National Forest for that particular build-up. By 1950 the herd had been reduced to near range capacity,

34,000 head. A shift in 1951 to allow hunters to take either sex, brought an estimated harvest of 12,000 head, but only a fifth of these were antlerless. The herd began to snowball again. By 1954 the total population had climbed to an estimated 46,000 head of deer. That year a total harvest of 17,000 deer was reported on the Fishlake National Forest. There was need of such a cut-back. A stockman who has any consideration for his herd's health and his pastures' continued growth of forage markets the animals above the number the food available can support. So do state game commissioners if intelligent sportsmen support them.

This is the pattern of game management that is being demonstrated on forest after forest in the west, through co-operative planning among the U.S. Forest Service and the state game-and-fish administrators. Its counterpart can be found on all forests in the east. It is merely another fundamental in national-forest policy shown in actions taken and results achieved—the administration of our forest properties to produce for human use in many and varied forms the natural resource wealth we can derive from those properties.

Game management on the forests presents a particularly sharp and incisive example of the fundamental difference between them and the national parks, where no hunting is permitted.

It is a long time since I put away my high-powered rifle. Having worked with and lived with the wildlife of the Rockies for several decades, I have no heart in killing any of them. But because the score or so young lads in my field crews in the wildlife restoration program in our one state laid the bricks in building one of the pioneer—and revealing—study programs bearing on wildlife in the national forests of the west, I cannot be blind to the demands of hunter harvest of big game as a tool of game management.

What we saw, and what the record shows, on the Fishlake National Forest of Region 4 cannot permit one to let sentiment overshadow the hard facts. Wildlife management must be part of the job in our national forests, and hunting harvest a necessary part of that management.

IX

WHERE THERE'S SMOKE—

I

IF THE southwestern portion of the Toiyabe National Forest did not extend across the Nevada line to snuggle against the north side of Yosemite National Park, and by so doing, bend boundary lines around the 695,783 of this forest's 3,271,139 acres that lie in California, California and Region 5 of the U.S.F.S. would share a unique distinction. Both state and forest region would be identical. But the Toiyabe, being part of Region 4, spoils this chance of California claiming one more unusual thing; bits of five other forests of other regions inching over the state's boundary further deny the claim.

In a practical sense Region 5 and California are identical. That straying bit of the Toiyabe is more a part of the Great Basin than of California. The fragments of the other forests are more identified with other states. Therefore, if we raise the curtain of early history on the state of California it also reveals the historical beginnings of forest facts about this region. A glamor bright as the shine of gold bedecks California's yesterdays.

On or near September 28, 1542 two little ships sailed into the bay we now call San Diego. This was almost to the week 50 years after Columbus sighted land he thought was India. Both Columbus and the Portuguese captain, Juan Rodriguez Cabrillo, were employees of Spain. The Italian is famous; the Portuguese is less known. If you want to learn a bit about Cabrillo drive out from central San Diego to the tip of Point Loma.

You follow the arterial street that swings along the finger of land between San Diego and Mission bays. At the outer end, perched on the ridge above the neat Coast Guard station, you visit the old lighthouse, a national monument with an acre of surrounding land. This squat white tower was built many years after Cabrillo became California's first European visitor. But it has been given that explorer's name, and there is a tablet there that tells of his coming on that autumn day in 1542.

Six days Cabrillo and his party lingered in this bay, which he called San Miguel. Then, sailing north, he entered the bay on Catalina Island we now call Avalon. From there he made a side trip to the present port of Los Angeles at San Pedro, and he particularly mentioned something he observed which has significance in relation to forest events of today.

All the way north from San Diego to Avalon to San Pedro, even so far as Point Conception, Cabrillo and his men saw great smoke clouds rising above the mainland. It was so smoky in those parts where Los Angeles has suffered modern smog that Cabrillo called San Pedro Bay *Bahi'a de los Fuegos*, Bay of the Smokes. And as a further note linking his observations with modern times, those smoke clouds surely rose from lands now in or near the Cleveland, San Bernardino, Los Padres, and Angles National Forests, where there have been fierce fires, reported in many shouting headlines as they flamed.

Cabrillo and his party traveled on from "Smoky Bay," to his *Bahi'a de los Piños*. The Arm on the south side of this bay he named *Cabo de Piños*—the Cape of the Pines. Look on today's map; there it is, Point Piños of Monterey

Bay, with pines still growing there. Each year thousands of butterflies gather at these pines for wintering.

Cabrillo died on the island he had named *La Posesion*, victim of an infected arm broken while exploring ashore. He was buried on the island at a spot now unknown. The Levantine Bartholmé Ferrelo, who had been Cabrillo's *piloto mayor*, tried to carry on, following the seacoast an unknown distance northward, then finally turning back toward Mexico, arriving at Navidad the following April.

A third of a century later Francis Drake sojourned in California. In June of 1579 he swung into waters near today's San Francisco and found it a "conuenient and fit harborough." There he refitted his *Golden Hind* for further journeyings. And Sebastian Vizcai'no dropped by in 1602. But it was more than 160 years later, on April 11, 1769, that a vessel named *San Antonio* entered San Diego bay to found the mission that was to become the city.

Peaceful decades passed in pastoral and missionary expansions. Then came the Mountain Men, riding rough and far. They followed such leaders as Jedediah S. Smith, and where they rode they blazed trails followed by settlers from the east. In 1845 the last Spanish governor was ousted, and the following year, at Sonoma, J. C. Frémont lent his name to raising the Bear Flag of the California Republic. Soon came the news that the United States and Mexico were at war. The Treaty of Guadalupe Hidalgo then ceded the entire territory to the United States.

Treaty or not, nothing could have halted what happened next.

In that same year, 1848, James Marshall discovered gold at Sutter's Mill near Coloma.

I I

It PROBABLY goes against the grain of Golden State boosters to be second in any respect. *Texas does* have more square miles inside her boundaries and Alaska is bigger than Texas. But there are very close to 100,000,000 acres in California if you look at it as being flat as a map, which it is not. Every native son will agree that if you could level out its surface, there would be enough land in California to spread entirely over Texas and tuck in like a blanket on all sides. Alaska is another matter!

There are 19 national forests in the state of California. They are draped over the mountains. On the map-flat basis they contain 23,402,016 acres. That approximates about one fourth of California's official area.

On a relief map of California showing its main physiographic features, you can see how close are the highest point in the nation, Mount Whitney, 14,495 feet, and the lowest point, Death Valley, 280 feet below sea level. The high wall of which Whitney is a part, the Sierra Nevada, runs north and south near the east side of the state and tosses up a barricade to anchor clouds above some of our greatest forests. Farther north, clouds are caught over the ridges nearer the coast—the Klamath mountains in the far northern corner, the southern portion of the Cascade range east and south of the Klamaths. White-draped Mount Shasta accents the southern segment of the Cascades where spread 1,876,387 acres of the national forest bearing the mountain's name. The Lassen National Forest with its 1,382,630 acres is named for a peak at the southern tip of the Cascades, which is still rated the only "active volcano" in the nation. Its activity over the years has been mostly lazy smoking since it blew its top in 1914–15.

The tangle of mountains where the Klamath and Cascade ranges stack up together near the Oregon line throws a transverse upland across the northern end of the state. Practically all of these mountains are in national forests. North of Los Angeles there is another east-west height of land, the Tehachapi mountains and their sub-ranges. Between these two chains of mountains, the network of ridges and peaks in the northern group and the Tehachapi heights in the south, is the fabulous Central Valley—a trough between the costal range and the Sierra Nevada.

Between the Sierra Nevada to the east and the Pacific Ocean's shoreline are Fresno, the vast acreages of vineyards, the smashing scenic and geological spectacle of the Yosemite Valley, the hillsides that turn to gold as California poppies bloom after a winter of exceptional moisture, and the sequoia trees, until recently rated the oldest living things. A group of scrawny timberline pines took the longevity championship away from the biggest of our conifers. Luckily for all concerned these pines were also found in California!

The mountains and the lowlands over which the clouds sail with no delivery of moisture limn the pattern of the growth that covers the state. The maximum in precipitation is in the northern mountains; an average in some locations of over 100 inches is delivered as rainfall since the coast country, under the moderating effect of the Japanese current, is rarely so much as threatened with snowfall except at higher altitudes. But snowfall does hit some of the higher Sierra Nevadas, with measurements running up to 500 inches per winter. And from these highest points, it is possible to look almost into Death Valley where a maximum temperature of 134 degrees F. has been recorded.

The Yosemite Valley is one of the world's striking examples of glaciation. Concurrent with the scooping and grinding of this spectacular valley similar glaciers were sculpturing other parts of California's mountains. But there never was a sheet invasion of the state as a whole, as there was where the national forests have been established in the White and Green mountains, or where an entire mountain system was laid low in the Quetico-Superior country.

Because much of it never was scoured by the continuous sheets of more recent glaciers, California offers a nearly limitless opportunity for adventuring in the vegetable kingdom, from the tiny, microscopic algae or ferns to the sycamores, Douglas firs, redwoods, and the gigantic sequoias.

I I I

FOR those who follow the well-channeled tourist routes, the chambers of commerce supply an array of thumbnail descriptions that are accepted as typical of California countryside. These tell of vineyards, orange, olive, date palm, and other groves of fruit-producing trees, the famed "Redwood Empire," and the big tree belt. The desert country is described, as is that doughty plant, the Joshua tree, which is, in fact—as its spike of white flowers shows—a yucca plant.

California is kaleidoscopic; often it is panoramic as well. You round a curve in U.S. Highway 80 just west of Coyote Wells and there you gaze northeastward across a gigantic pool of pulsing color. Vision strains to reach to the far mountains that leap beyond a curtain of heat waves rising from the Imperial Valley. Traveling another road at sundown you pause on the pass at Panamint

Springs, look eastward toward Towne Pass, 30 feet short of a mile above ocean levels, through which the famous 20-mule teams dragged 36½-ton loads of borax. Ten days were needed to travel from Death Valley to Mojave, 165 miles of highroad hell. You can make the distance, with your radiator probably boiling like a teakettle, in a short half day's drive.

In full contrast to these desert vistas is a February day when the scud, gray as a monk's habit, races low over the off-shore waves on the Pacific where the brown pelicans, with set wings, ride the small up-drafts along the breakers as far as you can follow their travel. The fog and low-dragging clouds climb the ridges of the coastal hills. They crawl slowly over the tops, jettisoning their cargoes of moisture as they go. Or altogether different landscapes are found in the rain forests of the Klamath mountains and of the Siskiyous where they balance across the California-Oregon line. And just east of this almost tropical belt of rankest woodland growth is the county of Modoc. There rough, raw faces of dark lava show up in blurps and little cliffs formed where a liquid rock wave stopped and cooled. But over most of that lava little plants and frost have broken rock into soil, or wind had brought soil in from somewhere yonder, and there are junipers and pines of the dryer zones.

California and the national forests within her borders offer a constant parade of contrasts.

I V

THREE recollections of spots in California come to me as I think of what her wildlands hold. One is the Modoc country. We traveled southward one day of the early fall hunting season after being forced to stop overnight at Alturas because of an early September cloudburst. The next morning the sky was clear, with its blue shell far away. The junipers and pines on the hillsides were freshened by the storm of the prior night and seemed greener against the browning grasses and shrubs. Across the landscape there were the red dots of hunters' caps or shirts as they prowled the lava ledges and sharp-rock canyons, looking for the big mule deer of that locality.

I have never thought of those ridges with the somewhat open stands of timber as being within a national forest. Particularly in the northwestern part of the nation, where anything called a forest should have trees two feet through the butt at shoulder height, it would seem that these dryish ridges and draws couldn't possibly be in a forest. But I look at the map, and see with certainty, that for more than 50 miles south of Alturas, first east of U.S. 395 and then westward, the ridges are in the 2,028,070-acre Modoc National Forest, the largest in Region 5.

On another day, when the brown-skinned foothills of the Sierra Nevada showed a tint of new green, we visited the big trees—the giants of the vegetable kingdom. Man has made himself ant-like as he has built his steel-ribbed columns and towers. Many of these structures measure several times the height of these big trees. But man is the master of these high-rising shafts; if it is destroyed, he can rebuild the 1,250-foot-high Empire State Building, the 984-foot-high Eiffel Tower, or the central 4,200-foot span of the Golden Gate Bridge. But he cannot, by any of his technical skills, reproduce a 4,000-year-old *Sequoia* tree. It takes time, and sunshine, and the moisture from many clouds to grow these giants from their tiny seeds, which weigh 300,000 to the pound.

The idea of time comes thundering in overwhelmingly when your own 6-feet, 160 pounds, and three-score-and-ten years stand against a *Sequoia*. You feel time's impact beside a tree with a trunk three dozen feet across, a height nearly fifty times your own, and an age so great that it was a lusty growth when Sargon I started to build a temple to Bel at Nippur.

You tread softly in the presence of the big trees. The soil is like a cushion, and if you are not too engulfed in your thoughts you may note the sulfur-colored lichen spreading its rosettes on a bit of fallen branch. Or you see the ferny cushion of a glittering feather moss and a black beetle stomping along his Lilliputian highway. There is a sudden return of balance and perspective as you find your place in reference to the beetle and the big tree.

But you never quite escape the awesomeness of these trees. You will remember this forest. With just a little asking or searching you gather a welter of interesting data about these California giants.

The technical name of the big tree has been a matter of dispute. Whether it is *Sequoia wellingtonia*, *S. washingtonia*, or the current *S. gigantea*, adds no height to any of them.

There are two *Sequoias*; the other is the redwood of the California valleys just east of the coastal mountains. The nearest relative to them is a resident of the southeastern lowlands, the bald cypress. Contrary to a still persisting belief that they are not now reproducing, the big tree, the *Sequoia* of the Sierra's western slopes, does scatter five to seven wing-edged seeds from under each scale of its little cones. The seeds do sprout, and there are young *Sequoias* in and around the many "groves" of the giants along the west side of the Sierras. There are also young redwoods in the groves of the coastal mountains.

The young *Sequoia giganteas* do not closely resemble their parents. They have a gray bark instead of that shaggy coat of the elder which is sometimes gropingly described as red-brown-purple. The crown of the young trees, until they are past the "sapling" stage of the *Sequoia,* is rounded, tends to be pyramidal, and is rather close in its growth. It does not show the long shaft of limbless trunk which develops later. And this younger form persists during the youth of the tree—that is, for 200 to 300 years!

Though the older *Sequoia* is moderately tolerant of shade, when it is little it must have sun. Often when seedlings tried to spring up under the interlocking, high canopy formed by their elders they were killed out, and the conclusion was reached that this is a doomed species.

The big trees are found in "groves." Breaks of from 40 to 60 miles occur between these groves. The groves are less widely separated from Kings Canyon southward. And here is the key to how this species, reckoned as having a family history reaching back 100,000,000 years, has come down to us while some of its genera died as continental ice covered the mid-continent or perished where the Petrified Forest lies fallen in Arizona.

Even in the cold centuries no continental sheet came shearing and grinding across California. Snows did pack in the high mountains and became ice that twisted down from the heights. It was such a frozen river that graved Yosemite Valley. It sliced through a stone nodule far larger than the national capitol and left it the Half Dome standing 4,770 feet above a point on the meadowy edge of the Merced river where that stream turns from its westering course to plunge suddenly almost due south through its Gorge.

These ancient ice rivers emerged from the hills, splayed out, and melted. On the higher ground, above the glaciers' thrusts, the *Sequoia gigantea* weathered through the cold centuries. There it persists today. The belts where there are none of these trees are where the ice tongues shoved out from the hills and killed out the flora of the earlier ages.

The breath of antiquity pervades the forests of the *Sequoias*. I remember particularly the splotches of sunlight on the forest floor, bright amidst a greater spread of mellow shadows. There was a stillness, too. The usual whisperings of the winds that so constantly move through a forest's treetops were far enough above so that they were only faint lispings. The qualities of a cathedral were all around.

My third recollection of Region 5 forests is, in a sense, stratified. Four times during recent winters we have driven west from El Centro and two out of four times, as we swung into that part of U.S. 80 west of Coyote Wells, our car's radiator boiled furiously. Even in January the walls of Carizo Canyon seem to glow with deep-held heat.

Beyond the final hump of this first climb, lies the downgrade into Jacumba where the town sits close to Baja California Norte's boundary. For a little way the road is flanked by pleasant valley fields, the deep green of the live oaks. It is after several up-and-down grades, crossings of saddles in ridges, that the brushlands that are to be the dominant plant association all the way to the coast appear continuous across the hillsides.

That brush is so thick and furry it would seem as if a giant could stretch out and roll down the hillsides on it as a child rolls on a grass-cloaked terrace. If you ask, you'll be told the brush is "chaparral." That is a catch-all term. Chaparral is found in many sections of the southwest and plant species that may be included in it vary with the locations, the amount of rainfall, rate of evaporation by warmth and wind—all the factors that determine what may grow in a land ranging from desert to rain forest.

The chaparral of southern California's hills contains mostly evergreen shrubs. Among these are the "wild lilacs" which are species of *Ceonothus*. The manzanita includes two species of *Arctostaphylos*, which also is the genus of ground-hugging kinni-kinick. Other shrubs include the holly-leafed cherry and a scrub oak, the latter shedding its leaves each winter. All this is mixed together in an utterly fantastic thick tangle. The bushes are 8 to 12 feet high and grow on slopes that are no more than 15 or 20 degrees short of perpendicular. Those slopes are so steep that if a fire starts at their base, they function almost like the back wall in a fireplace—a face of land up which drafts can be so fierce that flames flare as if from a blow torch.

And this brush patch—is *it* in a national forest? It is.

What is more, this bit of ground cover, this "forest" only a couple of man-heights high, probably is one of the most critical portions of all the national forests so far as water resources and fire are concerned.

This is the country that becomes so explosively dry that it practically explodes from a spark. In such country raced the Jameson Fire.

V

As YOU travel on U.S. 101 from San Diego to Los Angeles, you come to a junction where signs indicate that if you bear left you will continue to skirt the edge of the ocean. If you swing right, which is northeasterly, after three miles you will arrive at the village of San Juan Capistrano. This

iers shaped the valley where the Kern River flows from
Kern Lake in California's Sequoia National Forest.

With every available mean transportation, and with types of mobile equipm from pack horses to helico and parachute, the Forest S ice charges in to fight wil on the rampage.

For all its modern equipm and methods, our national est system has to depend or dirty, sweaty, often dange labors of the individual fighter.

The snow-draped crest of Mount Baker casts reflection in Baker Lake in Washington's Mount Baker National Forest.

Midsummer snow, a picnic spot, the timberline winds sifting through high-country evergreens — these beckon picnickers to Mount Baker National Forest.

Axmen, facing west, finally made their last
stand in the fabulous timber stands of forests
now within the boundaries of Region 6.

Skid roads formed by logs laid crosswise,
upper side made slippery by the boy ca
the Grease Monkey, were the first traffic-v
for the logging contractors in the Pa
Northwest.

e and mule teams gave way to donkey
nes, rail tracks, cables and drums, just as
n now has yielded to the power of the
l engine.

The toot of the busy little logging railway
engine was heard along the route logs followed from mountainside to tidewater.

Modern logging operation, characteristic of
the Douglas-fir region.

Modern forestry has adopted the practi
patch cutting in stands of timber made t
trees intolerant to shade. With the
cleared, the ground is exposed to the sun
the seeds sprout swiftly.

r, islands, mountains, timber — these
e elements of the scenes presented by
rests in Region 10, southeastern Alaska.

Land of rock and ice: the highest portions of
the forests in Region 10 send spectacular
glaciers winding down to the sea.

New Eddystone Rock, in the Tongass National Forest near Ketchikan, Alaska, is a landmark along the famed Inside Passage.

Two logs from the mountainside come s ly by high-slung cableway to begin journey from Alaska to faraway commun

is the name of a famous Franciscan mission founded in 1776—the mission of the swallows. According to legend they leave on October 23, Saint John's Day, to winter in lands farther south, returning the following March 19, which is Saint Joseph's Day.

Another junction is located at this point. It is the joining of Arroyo Trabuco and a creek channel named the San Juan. Both creek channels may have dry or nearly dry beds during many weeks of little rain. They carry rushing waters when the heavy squalls of the rainy season swipe across the landscape like very wet, very gray and opaque curtains.

Travel up Arroyo Trabuco to the highest point of the Santa Ana Mountains and you will be at the apex of Santiago Peak, 5,696 feet above mean sea level. The peak is on the boundary line between Orange County to the west and Riverside County to the east. Atop it is a principal fire-lookout station of the Cleveland National Forest.

When the weather is clear, you may see the land tumble away on the west to the Pacific Ocean. To the east are orange groves and vineyards. San Jacinto mountian farther to the east blocks any chance of seeing the green spot on the desert that is Palm Springs. Northward the land steps up to the San Bernardino Mountains, a northerly section of this national forest. Looking southeast, you may see Palomar Mountain in a main division of the Cleveland National Forest, where the astronomers explore infinity. You also look southeasterly to where the brush-matted slopes and ridges rise above the dry, closed basin, which when it rains sufficiently may become in truth Lake Elisnore.

Shortly before 1:00 P.M. August 30, 1954, Al Montoya, who was on Santiago lookout, glanced along the east face of the Santa Ana mountains. Quickly he took a second look.

He hesitated a few seconds to be sure his first glimpse had given him a true warning. It was a day when fires could flare up to singe and sear whole mountain sides. He had to be certain the puff of smoke that had shot up from somewhere near McVicker and Leach Canyons near Lake Elisnore was wildfire; it certainly was no time for anyone to risk controlled burning of any kind!

The smoke could forewarn of a dangerous fire. The slopes surrounding McVicker and Leach Canyons are very steep. The temperature reading that day had been reported as 98 degrees and the relative humidity was down to 15 per cent.

At precisely 1:03 P.M. Montoya reported the start of one of the hottest forest fires to hit southern California in recent years. The lives of communities below these brush slopes are at stake when such a fire breaks loose. In the battles to beat down the red flames human beings often reveal their capacity for great heroism and become burned sacrifices to someone's carelessness in letting sparks or flames escape to become destroying wildfire.

The 1954 blaze above Lake Elisnore basin—known in U.S.F.S. circles as the Jameson Fire—has been considered typical of the fires that curse the four national forests near the coast and south from Monterey to the boundary of Mexico.

The Jameson Fire can be presented in three scenes. The first is a brief chronology of how fire crews, swift-moving as the high-speed gears of a big machine, hit the field after Montoya's warning call. The second is of the damage the fire did before it was smothered. The third is what was done to prevent the secondary curse of floods that may descend from the tender, critical slopes if the sides of a basin remain "tin roof" and storms bring a deluge.

The Cleveland National Forest had two Fire Dispatchers. Kenneth G. Seebold was on the job at Escondido and took the report from Al Montoya that a big fire was imminent. Seebold reached for the "fire plan"—a plotting of the manpower and equipment organization which is on file in all forest offices, well studied and integrated in all parts, ready for the day the call to battle sounds.

A forest guard station is located at El Cariso, only 1½ miles from where Montoya had spotted the first smoke plume. Seebold threw everything located at the guard station, including a water tanker, into the first smash at the flames.

The San Juan fire unit, 37 miles distant, came next, the second organized outfit to go into counter-attack against the growing fire.

A bulldozer was ordered in. Paul Dryden, the Assistant Fire Control Officer based at Santa Ana, got his call to head for Elisnore. Two 40-man crews came next. This much of an anti-fire army was on the move when Alvin F. Wright, the Fire Control Officer of the Cleveland National Forest, was alerted.

Meanwhile a motorist reported the fire to the local headquarters of the California State Division of Forestry. Truman Holland of State Forestry and his two ranger associates hit the pike with a bulldozer and six 250-gallon tank trucks.

It was now 1:29 P.M. Only 26 minutes had passed since Montoya gave the alarm. In that time the fire had shown its red teeth; it was hungry, and it was becoming a giant. As soon as he arrived at the fire, Holland radioed for four additional tank trucks.

At the point of the fire, which still was small and with good breaks might have been contained, a bulldozer was blunting that flaming point. By shoving into the face of the flames, poking brush, soil and rock in against them, there

could be a roll-back that would wrap up this most vital segment of the swiftly made fire line. Then the cable that
controlled the blade snapped. It was equivalent to ham-
stringing the bulldozer. Twice the operator tried to repair
that cable. At that moment the fire, as if its insensate de-
mon realized this was the chance to run wild, did just that.
The opportunity to hold it to a little one was gone in that
moment. It roared into a major fire as if driven by all the
winds of a blast furnace.

Two hours after the lookout's call Seebold had tele-
phoned a caterer at Santa Ana, and by 3:00 P.M. that establishment had its facilities preparing 100 lunches and an
equal number of hot dinners. The fire dispatcher ordered
in men and equipment to establish the fire camp. The
caravan brought tentage, tools, food, even disposable paper
sleeping-bags.

By Tuesday night it appeared as if the fire had been contained. This was a second hour of near-victory. About midnight the wind reversed its direction. Leisurely it turned the
fire in a new direction and fanned it out of control.

Not until Saturday was the fire fully surrounded and
choked. A thousand men had been called in to labor on the
fire lines. The cost of the fight approximated $250,000.
The big loss was the watershed cover—the brush-forest
that one is likely to look at and exclaim: "That—a national
forest?" There had not been a major fire of record on that
particular watershed for some 43 years. Sprouts would
start from roots not killed by the fire within the following
4 or 5 years. But foresters estimated *nearly three fourths
of a century* would have to pass before the duff, the soil
sponge to trap the rain and protect the mineral soil below
it, would be fully re-established.

Meanwhile at least $2,500,000-worth of walnut and cit-
rus groves below the burned watersheds were in imme-

diate jeopardy. First, because their continued existence depended on the ability of the mountain slopes to trap the raindrops and send them into the soil mantle that was rather thinly spread over the hills, so that this water would come down underground to the mouths of the canyons where it could be pumped into ditches feeding the groves and fields. Second—and more threatening to those groves and fields—because of the danger of a smashing flash flood, with perhaps half of its volume the soil washed off the rock-core mountains. At the finish of the fire, 6½ square miles of watershed brush and tree cover was burned to the ground level; that much denuded area plus a cloudburst would equal catastrophe.

A brush fire in these national forests of southern California is more like a prairie fire than fire in big timber. The chaparral contains oily or waxy stuff. Self-generated drafts sweep up the nearly vertical slopes. These fires are so hot they often burn in one sweep the woody trunks of the shrub-plants which are 6 to 8 inches in diameter. It takes a trained, equipped army, with a campaign plan ready made, to battle such a fire.

And here is how the Forest Service gets braced to meet the challenge of such a fire.

At my elbow is the current chart of the Fire Control Organization on the Cleveland National Forest. Physically it is a simple mimeographed sheet of low-grade sulfite paper. But on that sheet is the entire diagram of who does what when fire breaks out. The fire-suppression staff is the first to go on a fire. A sort of auxilliary "home guard" is made up of other forest officers. All forest personnel primarily engaged in other jobs become fire-fighters in emergencies.

The organization that has its primary job in fire control,

heads in the Cleveland's Supervisor. Walter Puhn, Supervisor of the Cleveland National Forest, who acted as "field marshal" on many of the more spectacular fires in the southern part of California, traced out his organization diagram for me as we sat, one February day, in his office in San Diego.

"The Fire Control Officer is directly in command when we fight fires on the Cleveland," he said. "You see, he has his own key staff; the Central Dispatcher, the Assistant Dispatcher, and there are two truck drivers specifically allocated to his office.

"The 'line of command,' if you might call it that, ties back to my office. We also link directly with the Ranger Districts. The Descanso, the Palomar and the Trabuco ranger districts each has a fire-control assistant to the ranger in charge. These are the strategy and command officers. Below them on the chart are the working field men."

Referring to the Fire Control Chart Supervisor Puhn gave me, I note that the Palomar Ranger District has these officers who have specific jobs for which they are trained: 3 lookout men, and a clerk; 9 men trained as Suppression Crew Foremen; 12 tank truck operators; and add to these 5 patrolmen, 15 crewmen, and an Equipment Operator. The other two ranger districts on the Cleveland have in addition, a "Hot Shot Crew." This is made up of 1 foreman, 2 crew bosses, 17 crewmen, and 2 cooks. They are the front-line fighters that literally make a fire run to a blaze to stop it before it runs wild.

But that is only the beginning of the fire-fighting organization, which is in continual state of being made and kept ready. Each year all fire-control personnel have to go to school. Before they go in training for their particular job, they are examined for experience, the prior training they have had, and their adaptability for the job they may take.

All new men get 24 hours of basic training as part of the
first week of employment. The training never stops. The
men get at least 4 hours each week while on the job. Old
hands have to take a refresher course each season, in addition to the constant training on the job.

The units composed of these constantly ready men are
like "riot squads" on a police force. Usually they can stop a
fire while it is small. If it becomes big, a reservoir of informed and trained manpower is ready for action—and
woman-power too, for often women serve at vital spots as
telephone operators or, equally important, as cooks. The
array of equipment, the trucks, bulldozers, all the special
units and the work-a-day types that can be swung in to
back up the fighters—all these are carefully, fully lined up
for quick action before a fire breaks loose.

In addition to the publicly owned equipment, privately
owned tractors, water trucks, transports, pickups, airplanes, and helicopters are signed up for contract services
during fire emergencies. On the Jameson Fire even ready-
mix concrete trucks hauled water to feed the portable
power pumps. Doctors, ambulances, hospitals, and first-
aid crews are always on call. Food stores are asked the
amount and type of supplies they can furnish. All these
supplies and services are listed so that the dispatcher can
direct from his desk by wire and radio all that is needed
to place in the field and maintain a 1,000-man fire camp.

The prevention program is continually in action. Power
lines are patroled for weak poles that might break off and
drop a spark-spitting high-tension line on the ground. The
premises of those who live in the forest are inspected and
flammable material must be cleared from a 30-foot belt
around buildings. Incinerators must be screened, the ground
around them cleared. Campgrounds are "fireproofed." Prevention signs are tacked up. All firebreaks are cleared of an-

nual growth. Before fire seasons become critical, grass and trash plants along highways may be burned. And each year in the Cleveland about 40 "illegal dumps," where people have taken it on themselves to throw their waste papers and other refuse, have to be cleaned up.

Along the roads in the Cleveland National Forest there are some 55 developments each capable of storing 500 gallons of water. Other equipment used in fighting the fires is repaired and readied during the winter months. A whole manual, "Pre-planning for Forest Fire Control," has been worked up for individual units within ranger districts. Sectional maps show topography, truck and tractor trails, fire lines—every physical feature related to fighting a fire in that specific area. Pages of notes keyed to the maps tell of the type of growth, the pitch of the slopes, and as much information as can possibly be recorded, to help those who fight a fire in that unit. Also listed in full detail is the equipment available to fire-fighters in that area.

This is a glimpse, a bare listing, of what goes into planning the fire-fighting program before any telltale smoke rises. It was such organization, and the equipment to service it, that went into action when Fire Lookout Al Montoya gave the alarm on that August day in 1954.

The third scene in presenting the Jameson Fire deals with steep, fire-swept slopes where there had been the furry cover of brush. After the fire the slopes were covered with a layer mostly consisting of ashes. The open, rain-trapping duff which grabbed the showers and sent them down on their underground route to the wells that irrigate the groves of Elsinore was gone.

This is the part of the story which can be told with a happy ending.

As the fire smoldered to its end, 1,100 acres of the rich, grove-covered lands were in jeopardy. If a cloudburst of any size were to gush over those brush-cleared canyon walls, there would be a trundling, pounding mixture of rainwater and soil, mud filled with rocks, flowing down to the farmlands. That was the immediate problem. The tender soil had to be tacked down before such a storm came—and the rainy season lay ahead. A total loss of several million dollars from flooding and deposit of flood junk was an ominous possibility.

Government agencies and state, county, and local groups began meeting and planning while the hillsides were still hot. The immediate needs were of two kinds: first, a dam was necessary to hold back flood junk if it came, and a 20-foot dam to achieve this purpose was started. Second, there was need to get quick-sprouting, quick-growing cover over the exposed soil; anything that would grow fast enough and lace live roots through the topsoil would be welcomed.

The county had on hand some seed of annual rye grass and mustard seed. Both could serve. Seeding soon began where the fire had burned. Enough moisture came to sprout the seeds and to get the seedling plants established. They grew fast, and when the rains came there was a little wash-off, but no boiling, tumbling current composed of rocks, dirt, and wild water. It will take three-score and ten years, a lifetime, to get those burned basins back to directing the precipitation into the underground flow lines that will take it to the walnut and orange groves as they did in the past. But the seeds sown where the Jameson Fire burned did germinate, the little roots took hold, and the healing of the burned earth has begun.

There are other types of fires in other regions, and there are other fire-fighting organizations and plans for action when a fire breaks, but this story of the Jameson Fire gives a fair idea of how the U.S. Forest Service makes ready to fight fire.

It is doubtful if there is any one area in the nation where there is a fiercer type of fire to whip than in this chaparral, brush-type forest, found in the southern portion of Region 5. When you read of one of these in the Cleveland, San Bernardino, Angeles, and Los Padres national forests, you now may have a bit more of a mental picture of the red sheets of flame, the sweating, slugging work of men on the firelines, the racing of the water trucks and men to string out hoses to reach critical spots on the line, the whole sweep of people and things backing up those that fight in the very teeth of the flames.

X

THE EVERGREEN EMPIRE

I

WHILE strolling we often see traces of pigmy or giant natural forces at work. Small creatures trample trails through bluegrass jungles. Patient glaciers grind out holes in mountain sides which will be the chalices of timberline lakes. Wasps paste together their paper-walled apartments. Lava rivers overrun wide prairies. And by markings on charts, we may trace the course of mysterious rivers that follow established courses across the great oceans. Any of these may have a place in knowing a forest.

As in no other forest-service region, climate's impact has shaped the timberland draperies spreading over earth forms in Region 6. One of two dominant factors in this climate is an ocean current that begins to swing toward North America at a far distant spot in the Pacific Ocean. It may seem odd to approach Region 6 via an ocean current, but it is logical to do so.

The route of the North Equatorial Current passes the southmost of the Hawaiian Islands, threads westward through the Marianas, and approaches the Philippine Islands of Leyte and Samar. Here is located Cape Johnson Deep, a dimple in the floor of the Philippine Sea which probes downward to 34,440 feet below sea level.

Here the current splits, and one branch travels northeasterly along the east side of Taiwan. The Japanese call the next northeasterly extension of this ocean river Kuro-shio, the "Black Stream." It bumps into the southeastern hip of Honsku, heads eastward, and is officially named the North Pacific Current. We call this flow of water the Japanese Current, which warmed by equatorial sun and splaying against North America to either side of the Strait of Juan de Fuca, makes the climate of Region 6.

Each year an amount of water equal to a layer several feet deep evaporates from the near-by part of the Pacific Ocean. Cyclonic winds transport this water, as unseen vapor or as mists and clouds, across Oregon and Washington. In this way the skywater is dumped in an odd patchwork of different average precipitations, dictating a crazy-quilt pattern of forest types in Region 6.

A portion of central Washington with an average annual precipitation of only 6 inches approaches the recorded lowest rainfall norm in the nation. Less than a half-day's drive to the west, at Gray's Harbor, is the greatest average annual rainfall in the nation—*approximately 140 inches!* Between these extremes, and between sea level and the arctic tundra of the glacier-draped peaks of the Cascade range, are plant associations resembling those of rain forests near the equator and the scrub bush edging arctic barrens; groupings dominated by cactus and its cronies; others characterized by big ponderosa pines of the semi-dry intermountain mesas; still others that are very old, almost pure stands of stately Douglas firs.

The mountains—their height and their disposition between the ocean and the land to the east of them—determine most of this helter-skelter pattern of rainfall and the forests it supports. Perhaps the most graphic way to correlate the topography with the precipitation, and these with the plant associations, is to traverse Washington state, from east to west, as many visitors will.

I suggest Spokane, Washington, as our point of departure and U.S. Highway 10 as our line of travel.

I I

IF YOU have been following U.S. 10, the impressions of the forests, the lovely lake, and the moist and timbered country near Coeur d'Alene, Idaho, may linger with you until you are a few leagues west of Spokane. By the time you have reached Moses Lake you are in the area where the annual rainfall hovers around six inches. Still you may not fully sense how basically this is desert territory. The thin mantle of soil over underlying black lava has been scratched and this has been Washington's "wheat belt." Here and there the lava breaks through in little cliffs that are the faces of a flow where it stopped and cooled, or there are boil-ups that present a somewhat globular rocky face. Where the earth has been fallowed to produce a rain trap so there will be enough soil moisture to grow a crop the second year, thin spots begin to show and you may remember how, in the same belt of less rain just west of Pendleton, Oregon, a moderate breeze blowing on another day produced a full-scale dust storm as you hurried toward the road junction at Boardman and the palisaded corridor through which flows the Columbia river.

But around Moses Lake there are also lush fields and water in canals, flowing from the gigantic reservoir above the Grand Coulee dam. Since rain will not come abundantly to this part of the northwest, man has gathered it and the snowmelt flowing from the forests northward, in British Columbia, to irrigate Washington's new farming communities. Shade trees supported by this flow will grow here so that in the future less of the desert will be seen. Some unirrigated rough lands, dry gulches, and cliffy spots, will remain to remind those who give heed that the climate still is that of the desert.

Nowhere is the coincidence of mountains and forests better emphasized than here. In central Washington, in this in-between basin of the Columbia and its several tributaries, the rule is: no mountains, no national forests. It was not always so.

U.S. 10 crosses the Columbia river at Vantage. On the west side of the stream is the Ginkgo Petrified Forest State Park. Here is graphic contrast between the eons that have vanished and the moment of today.

The Ginkgo tree now seen in parks and arboretums, has been called a "living fossil." A number of species in this genus grew in China's long-lost forests at one time. They were related in one direction to the tree ferns, in the other to the conifers. Only the one living representative of the genus came through the world's climatic upsets. Other species left fossil remains, both in China and here in Washington state, the latter the record of great forests having lived here. It is as if time had scribbled a fragmentary note concerning yesterday's forests and dropped it here so that we might imagine a tree-covered landscape of the faraway past.

Passing on west through Ellensburg the highway soon enters the Wenatchee National Forest. This is ponderosa-pine country. Although the altitude increases as you continue along U.S. 10, you are not aware of it. Ellensburg is about 1,000 feet above sea level, which is typical ponderosa-pine and ranch country. Between there and Snoqualmie Pass, near Cle Elum, you sense that you are leaving the pines and moving into the fir-and-spruce belt.

Crossing Snoqualmie Pass, at an elevation of 3,004 feet, you suddenly see ferns under tall firs and shaggy moss on the trees, and you feel moisture in the air.

Several systems of mountain ridges run north and south and others run in other directions between Snoqualmie Pass and the edge of the Pacific. The clouds moving eastward first encounter coastal mountains—the lesser ones are really hills. But the Olympics, in the Olympic National Park, cannot be considered hills; their highest point, Mount Olympus, reaches skyward 7,915 feet from its base which is almost in tidewater.

On the west side of the Olympic range it rains until the clouds lighten so that they then rise and slide across the heights. In this way the rain forests are nurtured on the west side of the Olympic Peninsula.

On the opposite side, along East U.S. Highway 101, you may see patches of cactus and other almost-desert growth. There are streaks of country there where precipitation is some 15 inches per year—as little as the average precipitation in the southwest's Dust Bowl! It is as if the clouds that had rained so hard before they crossed the mountains were too exhausted to rain any more.

The timbered basins of Washington's national forests gather and deliver water to more than 2,000,000 people living in 110 communities. There are 111 water-power projects that rely on the forests to protect and deliver the water they require. Beyond that thousands of acres of farms and orchards are watered with snowmelt and rain gathered on national-forest lands and diverted to irrigation ditches.

Traveling through the climate zones and noting the plants in them, from Spokane to Hoquiam in Washington, provides the most extreme and the most abrupt contrasts in these natural associations. Travel easterly, from Gray's

Harbor to Longview, to Portland, then east into the Cascades, and you pass from rain forests to the saw-timber belt on their west slope. Almost immediately after crossing the Cascade crests—within a few miles of the swiftly dropping grade down to Prineville or Bend—you are in ponderosa-pine forest.

In Region 6, as in no other one, you will see these interlocking effects of climate, moisture, and temperature, of prevailing winds and topography, and particularly the effect of high mountains that lay their axis at right angles to prevailing winds.

III

IN Region 6 are the arresting remainders of forests that can truly be called "virgin." Here is the last skimming of the cream of the pines, firs, and spruces that were growing for decades or centuries before our kind came with axes and saws. Mature and stately, they were waiting to be ripped to lumber and nailed into ships and towns and houses.

First we highgraded the Norway and "cork" pines in the east and the north, and the loblolly and long-leaf and their relatives in the south. Then we felled the ponderosa and lodgepole pines in the middle and southern Rockies, the Englemann spruce and tamarack as well as the pines in the northern Rockies. In the great coastal forests of the northwest are the western hemlock, sitka spruce, western red cedar, and Douglas fir. Douglas fir intermingles with other species at the high elevations west of the Cascades. Here that odd conifer whose technical name, *Pseudotsuga taxifolia,* means "the false hemlock with the yew-like needles" grows at its finest. As "Oregon fir" or in the fir-faced plywood this tree is used in the walls or timbers of homes.

Region 6 holds the last, lingering timberland frontier of the mainland, where men of the breed of Bunyan swung their great axes. The axmen who felled the giants are gone now. One hears instead the chatter of internal combustion engines. They roar out of the bodies of great trucks and bulldozers. They racket in mechanical falsetto on the chain saws that fell the big trees in much less time than was required when the axes were used.

Within this region you now will encounter the new forest-management plan that is rapidly overrunning the patterns and programs of the older days. There is mechanization and much automation at every turn. Wood chemistry probes to find processes that will utilize every part of the tree—particularly the 57 per cent of the average tree cut for lumber which only a little while ago was never used. Here in Region 6 this new and headlong phase of our forest program is obscuring the type of timber operations which were dominant only a few years ago.

For at least a half century we have been told by the professional growers of timber that the best way to induce land to producing the maximum in wood is by what is termed "selective cutting." This technic—which originated in the early forestry of Europe—is still considered appropriate for ponderosa-pine forests.

In the past few years a revolution has taken place in the harvesting of some species of timber. It has come with "block cutting"—a clean sweep of all the trees when any unit is logged. You will see it on the mountains in Oregon and Washington, particularly where the tree communities are predominantly Douglas fir. The young of this tree demand full sunlight; only under full sun will Douglas seed germinate and the seedling establish itself.

In the basin of the White River north of Mount Rainier I saw blocks of the old firs left standing up slope to shed their seeds on clear-cut land below. I saw the young fir forest, rising almost as if it were the waters of a quiet tide, with tints in its thick, velvet-appearing nap as cool green as any tint of the ocean. Where a decade and a half had passed since the old forest had been clear cut, there was a fir-tree blanket on the hillside 15 to 20 *feet high.*

The patchy mixture of tall old trees, their darker green beside the fresh, plushy green of a young stand of firs, and near by some acres where the last tree has been cut off, the brown duff-blanketed ground ready for the seeds to fall, the young firs to spring up, reminds one not to cry out condemning the practice of block cutting. It is far different from the old "high-grading" of virgin forests in the central and eastern states. This is actually "farming": essentially a scientific cropping of forests.

Utilization continues from the time young firs are large enough for Christmas trees to the last harvesting of a block of Douglas fir. Beginning with the Christmas trees and continuing through use as poles, mine timbers, pulp bolts, spars, and piling, trees are used until those that are left are groomed into straight, tall, knotless, clear timber.

The shadow of Paul Bunyan may be seen among the workers in these forests. He would be here, surely, if anywhere in today's timber, because the deeds being done by his heirs are actually more prodigious than those Bunyan ever was credited with. He cut only the select timber and tramped on to new stands. Here, at the end of the trail to the west, his breed are staying, and growing new forests to meet the needs of tomorrows. And there, be-

side Bunyan, are the sons of the Timber Baron, and all
their cohorts—the men who have developed and put in
service the mechanical giants the better to utilize wood.
And they have adapted to their service the intricate process of physicist and chemist to break down wood and
then reassemble it in what some day will be an infinite
array of useful materials of wood, but not resembling it.

Region 6 is our Big Timber country of today. In the 19
national forests it contains there is a gross 26,991,323
acres and a net of 23,885,298 acres that we own through
the federal government. In the twelve months ending on
June 30, 1956, 2,632,800,000 board feet of timber were
harvested in these forests. Its value was nearly $50,000,000.
The timber was approximately four fifths of all timber cut
on our national forests that year.

I V

But there are other treasures in the forests of this region.
That people are learning of these, particularly of the
recreational resources, is indicated by the sharp increase in
recent years in the number of forest visitors. In 1952,
3,810,000 were tallied. Three years later the count was
5,192,000. At that time 1,000 designated picnic and camping areas were in use in Region 6 forests.

No single landscape, no one moment or hour, is con-
jured up as I think of Region 6. Certainly one of the
more vivid recollections, one that always seemed to me to
be a trademark of the region, became stamped in my
memory in July 1915. For several weeks while staying in
Salem, there was the daily blessing of afternoon's "Oregon mist." It came like silver curtains descending for a

quarter of an hour, rarely continuing for twice that length of time, and then with the atmosphere refreshed the clouds hurried on.

If the wrappings of the mists would part, we would see Mount Hood, Mount Jefferson, and the Three Sisters. Suddenly one day that scene was revealed. Hood, named by Vancouver for one of his party, stood high, like a great scoop of ice cream; Jefferson, named by Lewis and Clark, looked like a smaller scoop; and the Sisters looked like the makings of a banana split.

The mountain the Indians called a god, Mount Rainier, did not remind me of a dipper of ice cream. There is too much of the monumental and the supernatural about the mountain—which was named in 1793 by George Vancouver in compliment to Britain's Rear Admiral John Sprat Rainier—to relate its shape and whiteness to anything so quickly passing as a cone-shaped mound of ice cream.

Above all the other scenic features of Region 6's landscapes are these white-draped mountains. Shasta and Lassen, in Region 5, are the farthest south of these sleeping volcanoes, but the remainder of these heights are in Region 6. In addition to those I just named, across the Columbia to the north, are Adams, at 12,307 feet, St. Helens, 9,671 feet, both in the Gifford Pinchot National Forest. Rainier, fourth highest in the nation, is in the national park that bears its name and rises 14,408 feet above sea level. Eastward from the northern part of Puget Sound are Baker, 10,850 feet, Shuksan, 9,038 feet, and Glacier, 10,436 feet above sea level.

Perhaps only because of the time of day when I saw it, the point from which I saw it, and the perfection of the scene and setting, I would give to St. Helens the crown for sheer beauty. Rainier is gigantic. St. Helens is high-lifting and regal without being hulking and overpowering. Should you wish to see why I bestow the award of beauty to St. Helens, travel up the highway that follows the Toutle river east of Castle Rock, Washington. At the campground in the Gifford Pinchot National Forest, crank the telephone fastened to the tree and have the people at Harmony Falls Lodge come by boat to pick you up and take you to the far side of Spirit Lake. Do this at sundown, when shadows begin to become inky on the lake and the glaciers and snowfields of St. Helens glow against a Wedgewood-blue sky. This is one of the most scenic spots on this hemisphere.

Recently I stood in Washington's state park at Deception Pass, where the tides race erratically between Whidbey and Fidalgo islands. The great trees stood high, their heads so thickly laced together that a constant twilight filled around their great trunks. A path led down to the shoreline toward a beach facing toward the Pacific Ocean. The Pacific's main body was miles to the west beyond the Strait named for a Greek whose real name was Apostolos Valerianos—but the Strait bears the name Juan de Fuca. Perhaps that discrepancy is appropriate, for Apostolos, alias Juan, is suspected of never having reached that arm of the ocean as he said he did in 1592.

Should you have the opportunity, do visit the nook adjacent to Deception Pass where there has been no felling of the giants. Here is the great forest as it was; a fragmentary but a dramatic example of the woodlands that were. If you do visit here, never will there by any question in your thoughts as to the imperative necessity for setting aside to perpetuate their natural splendors some of the best and representative remaining portions of unexploited timberlands, ranging from these bosky parts to the ultimate in wilderness.

One January I traveled with Ken McLeod, a fellow conservationist, across the 1,772,637-acre Fremont National Forest of southern Oregon. To the north rose Fuego Mountain, 7,020 feet above tidewater; southward was Yainax Butte, 7,277 feet in elevation. Other heights flanked the road as we rolled along toward the little city of Lakeview, Oregon. Under a sky of deep winterish blue, the landscape was brown and gold and white where patches of snow lay in the shade. Grouped trees were green, but the color appeared a little rusty because of winter's winds. Some of the evergreens were ponderosa pine, but the great, spreading landscapes we traversed were conspicuously dotted with a tree I remember above other features—the incense cedar with its conical shape, its lacy foliage, its shaggy bark, its brownish color. At this point far east of the Cascades we were in the belt of lesser rain, but here—and also a little way east, in another portion of the Fremont National Forest in the Werner Mountains—the heights did stop the clouds that got over the higher hills to the west, and made them again give up their moisture.

Also among the vivid impressions of the earliest of my visits to Region 6—the one in 1915—is the tang of wood smoke on a morning breeze and its blue-gray haze in the air. In that year settlers still were burning stumps yanked out of the soil of the Willamette Valley. But smoke columns also fogged up from the burning pits where the edgings and slabs from the sawmills were gotten rid of.

Forty-one years later I again saw a few burners in use at Willamette Valley mills. Along the road to the saddle of Santiam Pass, burning mill trash gave off the incense that only burning pine can generate. These remaining trash-burners are on the verge of becoming extinct. Always they have reminded me of squat old ladies with voluminous skirts outspread as they sit knitting on a hassock, their pates smooth-rounded by a simple net bonnet.

These burners will fade out fast, for here is the part of the nation's timber country where "integration" is rampant. This is the process of keeping all activities near a company's mill, which will take and make use of everything from salvaged bark of the Douglas fir to sawdust and slabs. Solid lengths of logs too short to saw into lumber but long enough to be whacked into framing for furniture or into toys, shoe lasts, and tool handles are manufactured in associated specialty mills.

The pulp mills take all manner of tag-ends of wood which formerly were wasted. Into their big pressure cookers go slabs and edgings and other bits of wood, as well as the four-foot pulpwood "bolts" that are sections of the thinnings in forests being "tree-farmed." The stages of integration are extended from chipped wood to cellulose fibers and to pulp; from pulp to paper or cardboard; or from another grade of pulp to rayon and other synthetics. In the other part of the wood separated out by pulp-mill processes are the lignin and the pentose sugars. In these are hidden new compounds of fabulous promise which will be available once the chemists split these intricate portions of the wood and find ways to reassemble the fragments of the molecules.

Smoke hung above the trash-burners in the valley of the Santiam river in 1956, and I remembered how it hung over the valleys mixed with the morning mists in earlier days along the Willamette. But integration, a part of the new forestry which is so tied in with the forests of Region 6, is coming swiftly to arrive some day at a point where any mill that burns even trash wood will be archaic.

A few statistics are indicative of how much this is the big timber country. Such facts as these indicate the importance of Region 6 of the U.S. Forest Service:

There Douglas fir is the Number 1 lumber tree. Practically all of them are located in 55,000 square miles along the western sides of the two states, Oregon and Washington, of Region 6. Only one sixth of this land can be classified as being farmed; the rest is timberland.

Much of the 55,000 square miles is privately owned, and much of that is in the "tree farms" of the larger timber companies and in the pooled acreage of smaller holdings, but 16,000 square miles of this prime timberland lie within the national forests of Region 6. Some hemlock, cedars, and true firs are mixed in with the Douglas fir in the stands. Altogether these national-forest woodlands contain 40 per cent of the trees in the fir belt large enough to produce sawtimber.

For the most part, this considerable backlog of sawtimber is in the more inaccessible parts of the mountain territory. Some areas are checkered with the holdings of private timber operators. And here, at the south-side base of the Olympic Peninsula with headquarters at Shelton, Washington, is the Simpson Logging Company, a pioneer concern in having its own land grow much of its timber. And here also, under the specific law that allows such a co-operative set-up, is the first sustained yield program based on unified management of both private and federal forest land. This co-operative management directed so as to produce the most useable timber, is assured continuity under a 99-year contract between the company and the government. By this contract the Simpson Logging Company has assured timber production to keep it supplied with wood sufficient for it to operate at mill capacity indefinitely.

Region 6 has a great diversity of trees. Among them are western hemlock, western red cedar, Pacific silver fir, grand fir, noble fir, and sugar pine, as well as the Sitka spruce, western white pine, western larch, and an American yew.

Southwestern Oregon has 23 species of these cone-bearing trees. The redwood reaches its northern natural limit in this part of Region 6. Here also is that unusual member of the evergreens, the Port Orford cedar, which in years past was sought for coffin material because its wood gives off a scent resembling that of blooming roses.

Here also is the native California-laurel or Oregon-myrtle, a wood found only in this spot and in the Holy Land. In the early days the settlers tried to work this wood after it had dried, but they found that it was so hard and flinty it turned the edges of the axes. So they burned this wood, which is most lovely when worked into the smaller household articles. The Madrona, the Oregon blue oak, some of the ashes, and the maples are other larger native trees.

Any attempt to list the plant variety found in the under-story of these forests would lead to a seemingly endless recitation of names, common and botanical. The ferns are the impressive features of the more moist forests—among them the sword fern, deer fern, big bracken, and many others. And here too is the umbrella plant, with flowers before the leaves unfold and then leaves big and spreading.

The native orchids, the ladyslippers, and the pink cy-therea, can be found along woodland paths. And at the edge of clearings there will be the western form of the white dogwood, a large bush, or here more often a small tree. In the autumn of 1956 we saw the odd performance of this dogwood tree when a very late frost after its spring blooming caused it to bloom again in the fall.

Region 6 contains what is probably the greatest spread

of plant variety in the nation. This is a result of climate, which is determined by the combination of a major ocean current and the winds which carry inland vast quantities of moisture as vapor and clouds that are trapped in mountain mazes. There are the 19 forests in Region 6. They contain two fifths of the northwest's Douglas fir sawtimber and hold within their boundaries the more than 23,000,000 acres that we own in the two states of Oregon and Washington. And here are the last stamping grounds of men who live the legend of Paul Bunyan.

But today's Paul is planting trees, or running a tractor, or helping build roads into our national forests to harvest the mature trees that are not putting on any more annual increment of wood and must be harvested to give way to young forests for tomorrow. The heirs of the Baron are here on a board of directors, voting appropriations to achieve further integration in wood utilization, to press experiments further into how better to make use of all the values in the timber on their lands and also on the millions of acres of national forests in Region 6. Here is the very front of the new phase of forestry which has reached a high level in and near the national forests of the two states of the farthest northwest.

XI

THE GREEN GOLD OF ALASKA

I

THE mountain passes named Chilkoot and White were
snowy death traps for many stampeders who tried to cross
them during the Klondike gold rush. The high point on
either pass is on the boundary between Alaska and British
Columbia. From the passes, the defining line zigzags
southeasterly from crest to icy crest of the Coastal Mountains, the last in the series being Mount Dolly, rising above
the inmost end of the Portland Canal.

There the boundary line plunges off the heights, turns
westerly, and bisects the main fjord named Portland Canal.
Leaving this larger fjord the line slips along a narrow waterway between Canada's Pearse Island and the Alaskan
mainland. Before it runs on to fray out in the expanse of
the Pacific Ocean, the boundary performs an odd S-shaped
turn as it runs between Canadian Wales Island and Alaskan Sitklan Island.

The little waterway between Wales and Sitklan islands
is Tongass Pass. It is only one small loop in the tidewater
webwork lacing between the islands, capes, points, bays,
and headlands of southeastern Alaska; physically it is in-
significant among the many more magnificent channels
along this coast. But it was on Sitklan Island, facing this
channel, that the first United States military post in
Alaska, Fort Tongass, was built and garrisoned after the
purchase of the territory from Russia in 1867. Channel, or

fort, or both, preceded the naming of the largest of our national forests, the Tongass.

A recent tabulation shows that the Tongass National Forest contains 16,043,783 acres. It is approximately 350 miles long, which is the highway distance between Washington, D.C., and Cleveland, Ohio. The approximate width of this national forest is 120 miles, which is a greater distance than from Cincinnati, Ohio, to Indianapolis, Indiana. The shorelines within this one forest add up to 9,000 miles. When you travel through the "Inside Passage" to southeastern Alaskan ports, you are constantly surrounded by the timberlands of the Tongass.

Among the ports of Alaska that are encircled by the timber of the Tongass are Ketchikan, where the skies deliver 153 inches of precipitation per year, Wrangell, Petersburg, the Alaskan capital of Juneau, Skagway, and Sitka. Sitka has only 86 inches of precipitation per year, and Skagway has 26 inches. The timberline slips down the sides of the mountains this far to the north, and in contrast to the trees forging up to nearly 12,000 feet elevation in our most southern Rockies, the big woody plants stop at 2,000 to 2,500 feet elevation in the Alaska woodlands.

Within the belt from shoreline to timberline in the Tongass National Forest are an estimated 78½ billion board feet of commercial timber. This timber is by volume about 70 per cent hemlock, 20-25 per cent is Sitka spruce, and most of the remainder of the good timber is Alaskan Yellow Cedar and Western Red Cedar.

Three fourths of the commercial timber in the Tongass National Forest is within two and a half miles of tidewater and the low-cost transportation it affords. Most of the timber is on islands. Where mountains rise abruptly as on the mainland, the forest belt between shorelines and timberline is narrow. The best timber has been highgraded, and the remaining mature timber is made up of second-grade species of those of lower quality of all kinds. But these have their high value; they are suitable for pulp—and that is the type of "tree-farming" which lies ahead in the Tongass for some decades to come.

Where the trees stand thick the volume of wood per acre is high; often it reaches an estimated 40,000 board feet and that is considerable timber to have standing within an area about 210 feet square. Tongass timbered acres *average* about 20,000 board feet. But the stands are not continuous even where they are within the tidewater-to-timberline strip, which is almost as lush as tropical jungles because the climate is moderated by the Japanese current. Openings occur amidst the timber, many of them swampy spots that natives call "muskegs." Here are types of moss and peat used by the nurseryman, florist, and home gardener. These moss beds can be "cropped" just as trees can be "farmed" to assure maintained yields.

The pulp potential of the Tongass has taken the spotlight among the forest's natural resources in recent years. Timbermen refer enthusiastically to pulpwood forests as Alaska's "green gold." Promoters and leaders of commerce have, as a rule, taken a second look at the timberlands and seen a promise of "gold" in them only after other, more readily exhaustible natural wealth has approached serious stages of depletion. So it has been in our newest state.

Alaska's record, from its discovery to the present, follows this general pattern. In successive surges, different types of wealth have taken the center of the stage in this great land once called "Seward's Folly."

I I

A FAMILIAR pattern of public hullabaloo followed the signing of the purchase treaty with Russia on March 30, 1867. One sentence of the "minority report" in Congress is: "The treaty-making power (of the executive department) can no more bind Congress to pass a law than Congress can bind it to make a treaty." In welkin-ringing speeches, members of Congress called Alaska "Seward's Folly" and "Seward's Ice Box." The treaty was made, but Congress fumed over providing the $7,200,000 to pay for the purchase.

The treaty and sale were finally ratified. On Friday, October 18, 1867, the U.S. steamer *John L. Stephens* chugged into the bay at Novo Arkhangelsk (which was to become Sitka), landing dignitaries and a company of U.S. Infantry. Among the dignitaries were Captain Alexei Pestchourof, the Russian Commissioner, and General L. H. Rousseau, representing the United States. With flourishes, the party marched to where the Russian garrison was drawn up before the Governor's residence, troops of the two countries faced the Russian flag where it floated above the rock summit, orders snapped, and the flag was lowered. A brief declaration of transfer of the territory to the United States was made, the transfer was accepted, the troops fired a salute to the lowered emblem, the Stars and Stripes were then hauled to the top of the flagpole, another salute was fired to the new flag, and Alaska's 571,065 square miles of land and 586,400 square miles of water became part of the United States.

Still the principal commerce of the territory remained furs and fish. Gold had been found, but as in California and Colorado the mere knowledge of the presence of gold did not start the stampede. If the wealth that existed in forests was given a second glance it probably was because they were unuseful jungles so far as the earlier Alaskan-Americans were concerned.

A special Treasury agent, reporting to Congress in 1869, showed the low regard in which Alaska was commonly held. "As a financial measure," he said, "it might not be the worst policy to abandon the territory for the present."

For some years the United States seemed not to know quite what to do with Alaska. Then on August 16, 1896, a man named G. W. Cormack, who was prospecting for gold on a creek that acquired the name "Bonanza," found what he was looking for. By the following June the news had seeped out to distant places. The stampede to "The Klondike" broke loose and ran wild toward the headwaters of the Yukon.

Interestingly, Bonanza Creek is part of the drainage basin of Klondike Creek, which in turn joins the Yukon river, flowing in from the east above Dawson—all of this historical gold-rush territory is in Canada! It was, nevertheless, the Alaska Gold Rush. Gold was found near Nome in 1899, and the Fairbanks "strike" was made in 1902. The stampede became Alaskan in fact.

As the fur bonanzas and the fortunes made from fisheries had waned before, so did gold mining in its turn. By 1915, when the Alaskan Railroad was built as a government project, fisheries had gained first position in territorial economy.

As late as 1950, fisheries still held first place in Alaska's business fields. Then began the change that brought the "green gold" of the woodlands into the headlines. A new era had begun, with the Tongass and Chugach national forests underwriting this modern stampede to Alaska. A half-dozen major wood-using corporations and all their stockholders are deeply interested in this stampede. Beyond companies and investors, everyone who reads newspapers, buys milk in cardboard cartons, and wears anything made of rayon, also must have a personal interest in this new "gold rush." In the days ahead you are most likely to be using products that had their beginnings in the great trees of the Tongass and Chugach national forests, which are the whole of Region 10 of the U.S. Forest Service.

I I I

IN THE first decade of the twentieth century the wealth of the Alaskan forests was in the headlines. The historic conflict between Pinchot and Ballinger, between conservation and exploitation for private gain was over spurious mining claims that Clarence Cunningham had staked in the Chugach forest. Ostensibly the claims were located on coal deposits. Although entered under laws dealing with the development of mineral resources, the claims were actually a way of acquiring the tremendous timber values on the land.

The fight that centered on the claims of Cunningham on the Chugach did more than stop grabbing of public forest properties; it was the issue on which Teddy Roosevelt broke his political ties with William Howard Taft, formed the Bull Moose party, split the Republican vote, and indirectly brought about the election of Woodrow Wilson.

Over the years—back even to the Russian company's days—there was highgrading of Alaskan timber. The two world wars sent men into these woods, seeking the straight-grained spruce that was needed for the parts of certain airplanes. That accounts for the fact that the older timber that remains in the national forests of Region 10 is less than top grade. But it is the sort of timber that supplies the finest cellulose fiber and fulfills myriads of other uses after it is fully processed.

Unless a map is fairly detailed it does not show how the Tongass National Forest spreads almost totally over the "panhandle" of Alaska. The map must be detailed to show the islands that contain the bulk of the Tongass timber. Labyrinthian is the most accurate term to describe the channels, passes, inlets, sounds, and all the other broad, narrow, deep, shallow, big, and little fingers of the Pacific Ocean into the shorelines of the Tongass. Looking at the map one sees only very small areas of white that are non-forest around the several towns within its outside bound-aries. To me the islands and shoreline as shown on that map suggest the lacy, serrated and lobed twigs and leafage of a cut-leaf birch tree.

A provision in the laws governing the utilization of Alaskan resources requires a type of management insuring that timber remains a permanent resource of the territory. Furthermore, there are regulations applied by the Secre-tary of Agriculture, based on statutes, that make it man-datory the timber shall undergo first steps of processing locally.

Alaska's smaller national forest, the Chugach, contains timber that, for the most part, will be utilized within the state. It is assigned, by implication and management plans, to Alaskan uses. From the Tongass the "green gold" of the timbermen goes to the mills and then on into world commerce.

The first major pulp project is that of the Ketchikan Pulp Company and is located adjacent to the city of Ketchikan. This company is a joint venture of the Puget Sound Pulp and Timber Company of Bellingham, Washington, and the American Viscose Corporation of Philadelphia, Pennsylvania. It began operations in 1954.

This plant is of the newest type, employing what is known as the "MgO Process." This process almost completely eliminates the waste "liquor" that in the past has polluted streams and inlets until practically all aquatic life was destroyed. By substituting magnesium oxide (for the calcium carbonate that still is used in older mills) in the cooking "liquor" that separates wood's lignin and pentose sugars from cellulose fibers, the spent sulphite liquor burns in the fire chambers of huge pulp plant boilers as would high-grade fuel oils. Pollution of waters is reduced to a negligible factor, the power plants of the mills are supplied with readily available fuel, and the valuable magnesium is recovered and rechanneled into the process.

The plant at Ketchikan has a daily capacity of 400 tons of dissolving pulp. This is the high-grade type of pulp which goes into rayon and its relatives in fabrics and plastics. The plant cost more than $50,000,000 to construct and it has a contract with the U.S. Forest Service for a total of 8,000,000,000 board feet of timber to be harvested from the Tongass—which is a 50-year supply. By the time this timber becomes pulp, the young trees on first cut-over lands will have reached a size that allows them to begin to supply a new harvest under the "tree-farm" type of management.

Another corporation, the Pacific Northern Timber Company, arranged in the early 1950s to contract for 3,000,000,000 board feet of Tongass timber. Their program of development includes directing the sawtimber of better grades to a sawmill, other logs to their veneer mill to be made into plywood, and the parts of the wood not used in these processes to the 100-ton pulp mill that is part of this company's integrated operation.

The Georgia Pacific Company, another of the larger timber-using enterprises, made plans in the mid-1950s to operate in Alaska, and planned to utilize 7,500,000,000 board feet from the Tongass. This would supply a 500-ton pulp mill located at Juneau.

And in 1953 a group of pulp and rayon manufacturers organized the Alaska Pulp Company, Ltd. of Tokyo, Japan, with the objective of establishing a pulp-and-lumber enterprise in Alaska. In December of that year this concern became the parent company of the Alaska Lumber and Pulp Company formed under Alaskan laws. The Alaskan company leased an idle sawmill located at Wrangel, began to purchase timber from independent loggers in the vicinity, and planned to use between 20-30,000,000 board feet of timber yearly.

While peltry, gold, and fisheries represented Alaska's wealth in various periods, the green treasure of the forests waited patiently to assume a significant position in territorial, and even world economy. While other resources held prominence the green gold of the forests grew all around, and with modern forest management it can continue to do so.

Values other than useful wood exist in the national forests of Alaska. The salmon pack, an estimated 50 per cent of which is dependent on the waters of the two national forests, has an annual worth of well above $50,000,000 per year. Removal by the best methods of the timber cloaking the watersheds within the forests is closely linked to maintenance of the salmon resource. Wrongly done, logging can grievously damage the soil mantle on the steep slopes above the spawning streams. Rain can sluice away the earth if the slopes are scarred and exposed to excessive erosion. The mud-blanketing of the gravel beds that are the incubators of the salmon hordes, can wipe out multiple millions of these food fishes—and of this the foresters are aware.

They know too of the potential sources of power that are at hand in the galloping, plunging waters coming from the heights—millions of horsepower as yet unharnessed. These have their contribution to make to Alaska's pulp industry. With the great snowfields and ice fields above, the constant flow of power from the Alaskan rivers within the forests is guaranteed as positively as such natural facilities may be.

To all this material wealth must be added Alaska's wild life. The word "Kenai" holds special significance for both naturalist and sportsman. On the map Kenai is both a peninsula and a division of the Chugach National Forest. Twenty-five-mile-long Kenai lake, which can be reached from Seward by road, railway, and float plane, is in the center of this division of the Chugach.

The famous Alaskan moose, the giant Kodiak brown bear (largest of the meat eaters), black bears, mountain goats, and mountain sheep are big game species of the landward side. Bird hunters find grouse, ptarmigan, ducks, and geese. Trout of the region are rainbows, Dolly Vardens, golden fins, and lake trout. King, silver, humpback, and red salmon are regarded as food fishes, but a king or silver on sport tackle presents as fine a battle as anglers may encounter anywhere.

Game species are but a part of the abundant populations of mammals, birds, and fishes in the Alaskan forests; the wealth represented by these animate dwellers in the timberlands is prodigious.

Finally, no production figures or dollar values, can be

placed on the scenic displays of the Tongass and Chugach forests. They are *the* Alaskan scenery the traveler traverses as a vessel cruises from the United States to Sitka, Ketchikan, Juneau, Skagway, Cordova, and Seward. A gap exists between the most westerly bit of the Tongass and the eastern district of the Chugach. But practically all other parts of the coastline are national forests, from the time ships enter Alaskan waters at the south until they dock at Seward. Against this giant backdrop of some of North America's finest natural spectacles of sea, clouds, mountains, and forests, one also sees the colorful life of the people who live in the more southern parts of the state, particularly the native people.

The names of places in the forests of Alaska tell their story, too. They are Russian, English, and Spanish names —there were expeditions from New Spain that thrust well up into the islands in the Tongass forest. But more intriguing than most are the Indian names—including the names of the two forests, Tongass and Chugach.

Or is Tongass truly a native Alaskan word? As the Cossacks moved eastward through Siberia, during the early seventeenth century, collecting peltry on that mainland and linking the land to the Russian empire, they encountered a tribe named the "Tunguse." Although Alaskan guidebooks credit the word Tongass to the Tlingit Indians, there is enough phonetic similarity between early-day "Tunguse" and later "Tongass" to suggest the name of the little channel. Tongass may, however, be a name from Kamchatka.

There is no question regarding the origin of the name of the Chugach; it is an abbreviation of the name of a tribe, the Chugachigniut, that inhabited the Kenai Peninsula to the delta of the Copper River. In another spelling they were the Sh-ghachit Shoit Indians. This particular tribe has been practically blended into the Tlingits—in the early days the name was spelled "Thlinkeets."

For many decades the forests of Alaska have waited without fanfare—gaining only a modicum of notoriety during the Pinchot-Ballinger struggle—to add their bounty to the natural wealth of the land that no longer can be called Seward's Folly. Rather than being what some might term a last frontier of our forests, the Tongass and Chugach are more truly a new frontier—with the Tongass certain to become the largest, one-unit tree farm in North America, and very likely the largest in the world.

APPENDIX

National forests by state, their acreage, the headquarters of the forests, the Region in which the forests are situated, and the national and regional headquarters addresses and locations.

STATE & FOREST	GROSS ACREAGE	HEADQUARTERS	REG.
ALABAMA			
William B. Bankhead	560,604	Montgomery	8
Conecuh	339,573	Montgomery	8
Talladega	851,122	Montgomery	8
ALASKA			
Chugach	4,732,359	Anchorage	10
Tongass	16,043,506	Juneau	10
ARIZONA			
Apache *	707,991	Springerville	3
Coconino	1,999,504	Flagstaff	3
Coronado *	1,794,194	Tucson	3
Gila *	518,483	Silver City, N.M.	3
Kaibab	1,780,474	Williams	3
Prescott	1,457,283	Prescott	3
Sitgreaves	883,919	Holbrook	3
Tonto	2,961,905	Phoenix	3
ARKANSAS			
Ouachita *	2,129,270	Hot Springs Nat'l Park	8
Ozark	1,462,077	Russellville	8

* The forest lies in more than 1 state.

State & Forest	Gross Acreage	Headquarters	Reg.
California			
Angeles	691,052	Los Angeles	5
Calaveras Big Tree	379	Sonora	5
Cleveland	567,103	San Diego	5
Eldorado*	885,847	Placerville	5
Inyo*	1,828,986	Bishop	5
Klamath*	1,895,427	Yreka	5
Lassen	1,382,630	Susanville	5
Los Padres	2,027,021	Santa Barbara	5
Mendocino	1,082,634	Willows	5
Modoc	2,028,070	Alturas	5
Plumas	1,413,022	Quincy	5
Rogue River*	56,206	Medford, Oregon	6
San Bernardino	812,633	San Bernardino	5
Sequoia	1,182,589	Porterville	6
Shasta	1,545,379	Redding	5
Sierra	1,411,905	Fresno	5
Siskiyou*	38,729	Grants Pass, Oregon	6
Six Rivers	1,086,785	Eureka	5
Stanislaus	1,100,330	Sonora	5
Tahoe	1,190,264	Nevada City	5
Toiyabe*	695,783	Reno, Nevada	4
Trinity	1,202,675	Redding	5
Colorado			
Arapaho	1,067,022	Golden	2
Grand Mesa	368,418	Delta	2
Gunnison	1,759,757	Gunnison	2
Manti-LaSal*	26,674	Price, Utah	4
Pike	1,258,825	Colorado Springs	2
Rio Grande	1,910,798	Monte Vista	2

* The forest lies in more than 1 state.

State & Forest	Gross Acreage	Headquarters	Reg.
Roosevelt	1,085,143	Fort Collins	2
Routt	1,264,850	Steamboat Springs	2
San Isabel	1,239,973	Pueblo	2
San Juan	2,086,474	Durango	2
Uncompahgre	1,051,295	Delta	2
White River	2,076,387	Glenwood Springs	2

FLORIDA

Apalachicola	639,736	Tallahassee	8
Ocala	442,679	Tallahassee	8
Osceola	161,814	Tallahassee	8

GEORGIA

Chattahoochee	1,518,417	Gainesville	8

IDAHO

Bitterroot*	461,145	Hamilton, Montana	1
Boise	2,950,568	Boise	4
Cache*	263,218	Logan, Utah	4
Caribou*	1,061,318	Pocatello	4
Challis	2,468,067	Challis	4
Clearwater	1,294,434	Orifino	1
Coeur d'Alene	802,177	Coeur d'Alene	1
Kaniksu*	1,059,382	Sandpoint	1
Kootenai*	48,851	Libby, Montana	1
Lolo*	466,718	Missoula, Montana	1
Nezperce	2,240,939	Grangeville	1
Payette	2,418,977	McCall	4
St. Joe	1,089,197	St. Maries	1
Salmon	1,790,944	Salmon	4
Sawtooth	1,790,357	Twin Falls	4
Targhee*	1,346,481	St. Anthony	4

* The forest lies in more than 1 state.

State & Forest	Gross Acreage	Headquarters	Reg.
ILLINOIS			
Shawnee	802,383	Harrisburg	9
INDIANA			
Hoosier	722,460	Bedford	9
KENTUCKY			
Cumberland	1,357,085	Winchester	7
LOUISIANA			
Kisatchie	877,066	Alexandria	8
MAINE			
White Mountain*	53,551	Laconia, New Hampshire	7
MICHIGAN			
Hiawatha	822,020	Escanaba	9
Huron	762,280	Cadillac	9
Manistee	1,254,855	Cadillac	9
Marquette	504,075	Escanaba	9
Ottawa	1,742,966	Ironwood	9
MINNESOTA			
Chippewa	1,313,643	Cass Lake	9
Superior	2,873,576	Duluth	9
MISSISSIPPI			
Bienville	382,820	Jackson	8
De Soto	1,213,740	Jackson	8
Holly Springs	462,040	Jackson	8
Homochitto	373,495	Jackson	8

* The forest lies in more than 1 state.

State & Forest	Gross Acreage	Headquarters	Reg.
MISSOURI			
Clark	1,972,296	Rolla, Mo. and Harrisburg, Ill.	9
Mark Twain	1,349,532	Rolla	9
MONTANA			
Beaverhead	2,216,401	Dillon	1
Bitterroot*	1,188,188	Hamilton	1
Custer*	1,196,569	Billings	1
Deerlodge	1,329,841	Butte	1
Flathead	2,625,402	Kalispell	1
Gallatin	2,129,750	Bozeman	1
Helena	1,156,679	Helena	1
Kaniksu*	491,376	Sandpoint, Idaho	1
Kootenai*	2,091,070	Libby	1
Lewis and Clark	2,031,604	Great Falls	1
Lolo*	2,599,057	Missoula	1
NEBRASKA			
Nebraska	207,263	Lincoln	2
NEVADA			
Eldorado*	400	Placerville, California	5
Humboldt	1,481,094	Elko	4
Inyo*	62,348	Bishop, California	5
Nevada	1,259,528	Elko	4
Toiyabe*	2,575,356	Reno	4
NEW HAMPSHIRE			
White Mountain*	798,291	Laconia	7
NEW MEXICO			
Apache*	1,009,553	Springerville, Arizona	3

---

* The forest lies in more than 1 state.

State & Forest	Gross Acreage	Headquarters	Reg.
Carson	1,288,009	Taos	3
Cibola	2,275,282	Albuquerque	3
Coronado*	72,492	Tucson, Arizona	3
Gila*	2,426,976	Silver City	3
Lincoln	1,444,316	Alamogordo	3
Santa Fe	1,362,993	Santa Fe	3
North Carolina			
Cherokee*	327	Cleveland, Tennessee	8
Croatan	294,610	Asheville	8
Nantahala	1,349,000	Asheville	8
Pisgah	1,177,303	Asheville	8
Ohio			
Wayne	1,454,976	Bedford, Indiana	9
Oklahoma			
Ouachita*	591,509	Hot Springs National Park, Arkansas	8
Oregon			
Deschutes	1,927,401	Bend	6
Fremont	1,772,641	Lakeview	6
Klamath*	32,119	Yreka, California	5
Malheur	1,275,913	John Day	6
Mt. Hood	1,183,886	Portland	6
Ochoco	980,846	Prineville	6
Rogue River*	1,148,292	Medford	6
Siskiyou*	1,350,440	Grants Pass	6
Siuslaw	878,161	Corvallis	6
Umatilla*	1,192,176	Pendleton	6
Umpqua	1,180,908	Roseburg	6
Wallowa	1,073,973	Baker	6

* The forest lies in more than 1 state.

State & Forest	Gross Acreage	Headquarters	Reg.
Whitman	1,568,433	Baker	6
Williamette	1,819,970	Eugene	6
Pennsylvania			
Allegheny	736,577	Warren	7
Puerto Rico			
Caribbean	65,950	Rio Piedras	TR
South Carolina			
Francis Marion	414,701	Columbia	8
Sumter	1,008,639	Columbia	8
South Dakota			
Black Hills*	1,325,558	Custer	2
Custer*	77,826	Billings, Montana	1
Tennessee			
Cherokee*	1,204,102	Cleveland	8
Texas			
Angelina	391,300	Lufkin	8
Davy Crockett	394,200	Lufkin	8
Sabine	439,665	Lufkin	8
Sam Houston	491,800	Lufkin	8
Utah			
Ashley	1,313,461	Vernal	4
Cache*	953,115	Logan	4
Caribou*	9,095	Pocatello, Idaho	4
Dixie	1,936,885	Cedar City	4
Fishlake	1,526,909	Richfield	4
Manti-LaSal*	1,312,935	Price	4
Sawtooth	92,403	Twin Falls, Idaho	4

* The forest lies in more than 1 state.

State & Forest	Gross Acreage	Headquarters	Reg.
Uinta	853,165	Provo	4
Wasatch*	920,560	Salt Lake City	4
Vermont			
Green Mountain	629,004	Rutland	7
Virginia			
George Washington*	1,544,776	Harrisonburg	7
Jefferson	2,364,881	Roanoke	7
Washington			
Colville	1,007,874	Colville	1
Gifford Pinchot	1,421,600	Vancouver	6
Kaniksu*	297,340	Sandpoint, Idaho	1
Mount Baker	1,851,400	Bellingham	6
Okanogan	2,090,631	Okanogan	6
Olympic	689,871	Olympia	6
Snoqualmie	1,538,142	Seattle	6
Umatilla*	321,875	Pendleton, Oregon	6
Wenatchee	1,523,340	Wenatchee	6
West Virginia			
George Washington*	161,236	Harrisonburg, Virginia	7
Monongahela	1,641,981	Elkins	7
Wisconsin			
Chequamegon	1,035,405	Park Falls	9
Nicolet	988,853	Rhinelander	9
Wyoming			
Bighorn	1,121,541	Sheridan	2
Black Hills*	199,466	Custer, South Dakota	2
Bridger	1,710,221	Kemmerer	4
Caribou*	7,273	Pocatello, Idaho	4

* The forest lies in more than 1 state.

STATE & FOREST	GROSS ACREAGE	HEADQUARTERS	REG.
Medicine Bow	1,398,288	Laramie	2
Shoshone	2,458,644	Cody	2
Targhee*	344,573	St. Anthony, Idaho	4
Teton	1,729,306	Jackson	4
Wasatch*	46,823	Salt Lake City, Utah	4

* The forest lies in more than 1 state.

NATIONAL AND REGIONAL HEADQUARTERS OF
THE FOREST SERVICE

NATIONAL HEADQUARTERS: *Forest Service, Department of Agriculture, Washington 25, D.C.*

REGIONAL HEADQUARTERS:

REGION 1. NORTHERN REGION: *Federal Building, Missoula, Montana. Embracing northern Idaho, Montana, northwestern South Dakota, northeastern Washington and extreme northwestern part of Wyoming.*

REGION 2. ROCKY MOUNTAIN REGION: *Federal Center, Building No. 85, Denver, Colorado. Embracing Colorado (except small part in extreme west), Kansas, Nebraska, South Dakota (except extreme northwest part) and major part of Wyoming.*

REGION 3. SOUTHWESTERN REGION: *510 Second Street N.W., Albuquerque, New Mexico. Embracing Arizona and New Mexico.*

REGION 4. INTERMOUNTAIN REGION: *Forest Service Building, Ogden, Utah. Embracing a part of east-central California, a small part in western Colorado, southern Idaho, Nevada (except a small area in the southwestern part), Utah and the extreme western part of Wyoming.*

REGION 5. CALIFORNIA REGION: *630 Sansome Street, San Francisco 11, California. Embracing California (except small part in extreme northwest and part in the east-central), a small part in southwestern Nevada, and a small part in southern Oregon.*

REGION 6. PACIFIC NORTHWEST REGION: *729 N.E. Oregon Street, Portland 8, Oregon. Embracing small part in extreme northwestern California, Oregon (except small part in extreme southwest), Washington (except northeastern part).*

REGION 7. EASTERN REGION: *Center Building, 6816 Market Street, Upper Darby, Pennsylvania. Embracing Connecticut, Delaware, Kentucky, Maine, Maryland, Massachusetts, New Hampshire, New Jersey, New York, Pennsylvania, Rhode Island, Vermont, Virginia and West Virginia.*

REGION 8. SOUTHERN REGION: *50 Seventh Street N.E., Atlanta 23, Georgia. Embracing Alabama, Arkansas, Florida, Georgia, Louisiana, Mississippi, North Carolina, Oklahoma, South Carolina, Tennessee and Texas.*

REGION 9. NORTH CENTRAL REGION: *623 North Second Street, Milwaukee 3, Wisconsin. Embracing Illinois, Indiana, Iowa, Michigan, Minnesota, Missouri, North Dakota, Ohio and Wisconsin.*

REGION 10. ALASKA REGION: *Federal and Territorial Building, Juneau, Alaska. Embracing Alaska.*

INDEX

Abnaki Indians, 61
absorption of moisture by leaves, 71
Acts of Congress establishing national forests, 11, 28, 32, 33
Agriculture, Department of: Bureau of Forestry, 17, 29; Division of Forestry, 27, 29
airplanes, use of, by Forest Service, 146
Alaska: area of, 270; gold rush, 271; purchase of, 270
Allegheny National Forest, 66
altitude, effect on forest types, 41, 185
American Association for Advancement of Science, 27
American Forestry Association, formed, 27
Apalachee Indians, 82
Apalachicola, Fla., 82
Appalachia, 55
Appalachian Club, 65
Appalachian Trail, 81
Appalachian Trough, 57, 68
Appomattox Courthouse, 70
Arbor Day, first proclaimed, 26
area: of all national forests, 3; of Tongas, 3; of Tonto, 3
Arrowhead region, Minn., 108
Atlantic City, Wyo., 171
automobile traffic in national forests, 21

Ballinger, Richard A.: Commissioner, General Land Office, 29; Secretary of Interior, 30, 272
bark beetles: control methods, 155-6; damage caused by, 153; life cycle, 156
Bartlett Experimental Forest, 63
Bay of Smokes, Calif., 230
Bear Creek basin, 7
Bell, John W., 145
Big Hole battlefield, Mont., 141
"Big Slip," fault line, 215
Biltmore Forest School, 80
Biological Survey, predator control by, 220
Black Hills National Forest, 162
blister rust disease, 151
Blue Ridge Mountains, 59
Bob Marshall Wilderness, attacked by beetles, 155
bog records, Superior National Forest, 114
Boise, Fort, 214
Bridger National Forest, 209
brown spot disease of pines, 97
Buffalo Bill, Pahaska Teepee, 165
Bunyan, Paul, 99
Bureau of Forestry, established, 17, 29
burning, controlled: eradicates brown spot, 97; prepares seed bed for loblolly pine, 97

Backus, E. W., 120

Cabrillo, Juan Rodriguez, 228

A Note about the Author

ARTHUR H. CARHART *is nationally recognized as a leader in the conservation field. Born in Mapleton, Iowa, in 1892, he received a B.S. in landscape architecture and city-planning from Iowa State College in 1916. After serving with the medical corps in World War I, he joined the U.S. Forest Service as its first permanent landscape architect in 1919. Four years later he resigned to engage in private practice as a professional landscape architect and city-planner, and began his long and productive career as a writer of books and magazine articles on conservation and the outdoor life. In 1938 he was appointed director of the program for Federal Aid in Wildlife Restoration in Colorado. Arthur Carhart's many books include* The Outdoorsman's Cookbook (1944), Fresh Water Fishing (1950); *and he won the Founder's Award of the Izaak Walton League for his* Water—or Your Life (1951), Timber in Your Life (1955), *and other writings about conservation.*

A NOTE ON THE TYPE

This book is set in ELECTRA, *a Linotype face designed by* W. A. DWIGGINS (1880–1956), *who was responsible for so much that is good in contemporary book design. Although much of his early work was in advertising and he was the author of the standard volume* Layout in Advertising, *Mr. Dwiggins later devoted his prolific talents to book typography and type design, and worked with great distinction in both fields. In addition to his designs for* Electra, *he created the Metro, Caledonia, and Eldorado series of type faces, as well as a number of experimental cuttings that have never been issued commercially.*

Electra cannot be classified as either modern or old-style. It is not based on any historical model, nor does it echo a particular period or style. It avoids the extreme contrast between thick and thin elements which marks most modern faces, and attempts to give a feeling of fluidity, power, and speed.

This book was composed, printed, and bound by H. Wolff, New York. *Illustrations in halftone printed by* Clarke & Way, The Thistle Press, New York. *The paper was manufactured by* S. D. Warren Co., Boston. *Typography and binding based on designs by* W. A. Dwiggins.